Songbird Eva Cassidy

Wise Publications

London / New York / Sydney / Paris / Copenhagen / Madrid / Tokyo

Exclusive distributors:
Music Sales Limited
8/9 Frith Street, London W1B 3JB, England.
Music Sales Pty Limited
120 Rothschild Avenue, Rosebery, NSW 2018,
Australia.

Order No.AM971960
ISBN 0-7119-9069-7
This book © Copyright 2001 by Wise Publications.

Music arranged by Matt Cowe.
Music engraved by Digital Music Art.

Cover photograph courtesy of Hot Records.

Printed in the United Kingdom by
Printwise (Haverhill) Limited, Suffolk.

Your Guarantee of Quality:
As publishers, we strive to produce every
book to the highest commercial standards.
The music has been freshly engraved and, whilst endeavouring
to retain the original running order of the recorded album,
the book has been carefully designed to minimise awkward
page turns and to make playing from it a real pleasure.
Particular care has been given to specifying acid-free,
neutral-sized paper made from pulps which have not been
elemental chlorine bleached.
This pulp is from farmed sustainable forests and was produced
with special regard for the environment.
Throughout, the printing and binding have been planned
to ensure a sturdy, attractive publication which should give
years of enjoyment.
If your copy fails to meet our high standards, please inform
us and we will gladly replace it.

Music Sales' complete catalogue describes thousands
of titles and is available in full colour sections by subject,
direct from Music Sales Limited.
Please state your areas of interest and send a cheque/
postal order for £1.50 for postage to: Music Sales Limited,
Newmarket Road, Bury St. Edmunds, Suffolk IP33 3YB.

www.musicsales.com

Guitar Tablature Explained

Guitar music can be notated three different ways: on a musical stave, in tablature, and in rhythm slashes

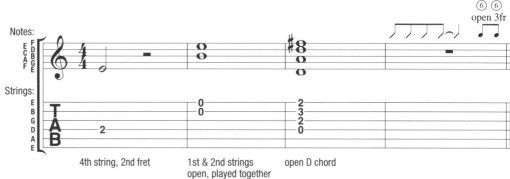

RHYTHM SLASHES are written above the stave. Strum chords in the rhythm indicated. Round noteheads indicate single notes.

THE MUSICAL STAVE shows pitches and rhythms and is divided by lines into bars. Pitches are named after the first seven letters of the alphabet.

TABLATURE graphically represents the guitar fingerboard. Each horizontal line represents a string, and each number represents a fret.

definitions for special guitar notation

SEMI-TONE BEND: Strike the note and bend up a semi-tone (1/2 step).

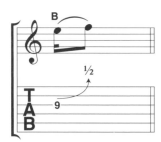

WHOLE-TONE BEND: Strike the note and bend up a whole-tone (whole step).

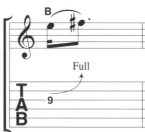

GRACE NOTE BEND: Strike the note and bend as indicated. Play the first note as quickly as possible.

QUARTER-TONE BEND: Strike the note and bend up a 1/4 step.

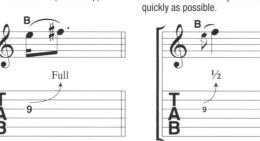
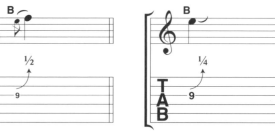

BEND & RELEASE: Strike the note and bend up as indicated, then release back to the original note.

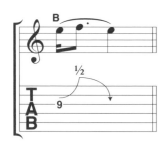

COMPOUND BEND & RELEASE: Strike the note and bend up and down in the rhythm indicated.

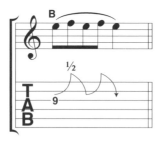

PRE-BEND: Bend the note as indicated, then strike it.

PRE-BEND & RELEASE: Bend the note as indicated. Strike it and release the note back to the original pitch.

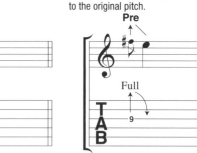

UNISON BEND: Strike the two notes simultaneously and bend the lower note up to the pitch of the higher.

BEND & RESTRIKE: Strike the note and bend as indicated then restrike the string where the symbol occurs.

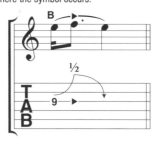

BEND, HOLD AND RELEASE: Same as bend and release but hold the bend for the duration of the tie.

BEND AND TAP: Bend the note as indicated and tap the higher fret while still holding the bend.

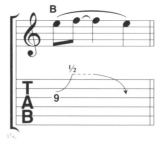

VIBRATO: The string is vibrated by rapidly bending and releasing the note with the fretting hand.

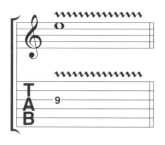

HAMMER-ON: Strike the first (lower) note with one finger, then sound the higher note (on the same string) with another finger by fretting it without picking.

PULL-OFF: Place both fingers on the notes to be sounded, Strike the first note without picking, pull the finger off to sound the second (lower) note.

LEGATO SLIDE (GLISS): Strike the first note and then slide the same fret-hand finger up or down to the second note. The second note is not struck.

NOTE: The speed of any bend is indicated by the music notation and tempo.

4

SHIFT SLIDE (GLISS & RESTRIKE): Same as legato slide, except the second note is struck.

TRILL: Very rapidly alternate between the notes indicated by continuously hammering on and pulling off.

TAPPING: Hammer ("tap") the fret indicated with the pick-hand index or middle finger and pull off to the note fretted by the fret hand.

PICK SCRAPE: The edge of the pick is rubbed down (or up) the string, producing a scratchy sound.

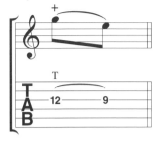

MUFFLED STRINGS: A percussive sound is produced by laying the fret hand across the string(s) without depressing, and striking them with the pick hand.

NATURAL HARMONIC: Strike the note while the fret-hand lightly touches the string directly over the fret indicated.

PINCH HARMONIC: The note is fretted normally and a harmonic is produced by adding the edge of the thumb or the tip of the index finger of the pick hand to the normal pick attack.

HARP HARMONIC: The note is fretted normally and a harmonic is produced by gently resting the pick hand's index finger directly above the indicated fret (in parentheses) while the pick hand's thumb or pick assists by plucking the appropriate string.

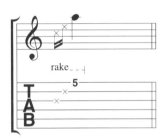

PALM MUTING: The note is partially muted by the pick hand lightly touching the string(s) just before the bridge.

RAKE: Drag the pick across the strings indicated with a single motion.

TREMOLO PICKING: The note is picked as rapidly and continuously as possible.

ARPEGGIATE: Play the notes of the chord indicated by quickly rolling them from bottom to top.

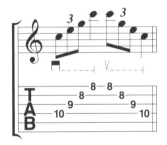
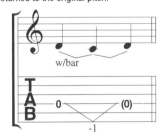
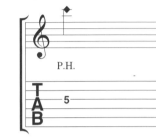

SWEEP PICKING: Rhythmic downstroke and/or upstroke motion across the strings.

VIBRATO DIVE BAR AND RETURN: The pitch of the note or chord is dropped a specific number of steps (in rhythm) then returned to the original pitch.

VIBRATO BAR SCOOP: Depress the bar just before striking the note, then quickly release the bar.

VIBRATO BAR DIP: Strike the note and then immediately drop a specific number of steps, then release back to the original pitch.

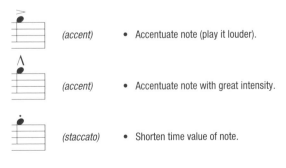

additional musical definitions

(accent)	• Accentuate note (play it louder).	
(accent)	• Accentuate note with great intensity.	
(staccato)	• Shorten time value of note.	
	• Downstroke	
V	• Upstroke	

D.%. al Coda

D.C. al Fine

tacet

1. **2.**

- Go back to the sign (%), then play until the bar marked *To Coda* ⊕ then skip to the section marked ⊕ *Coda*.

- Go back to the beginning of the song and play until the bar marked *Fine* (end).

- Instrument is silent (drops out).

- Repeat bars between signs.

- When a repeated section has different endings, play the first ending only the first time and the second ending only the second time.

NOTE: Tablature numbers in parentheses mean: 1. The note is sustained, but a new articulation (such as hammer on or slide) begins.
2. A note may be fretted but not necessarily played.

5

Fields Of Gold

Words & Music by Sting

*Symbols in parentheses represent chord names with respect to capoed gtr. (Tab 0 = capo 7th fret)
Symbols above represent actual sounding chords

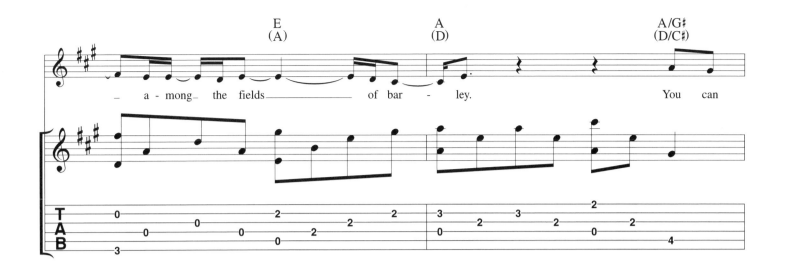

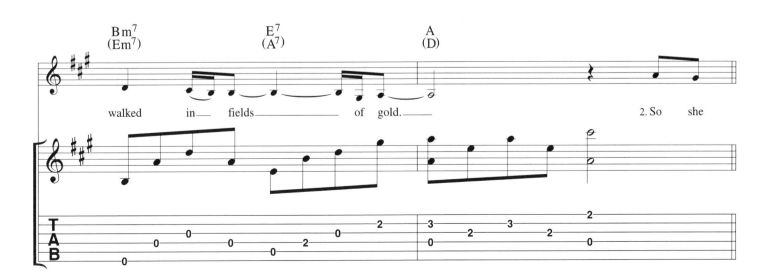

Verse

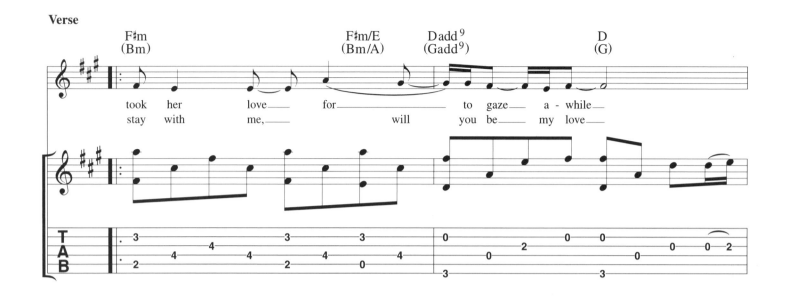

took her love___ for_____ to gaze___ a - while___
stay with me,___ will you be___ my love___

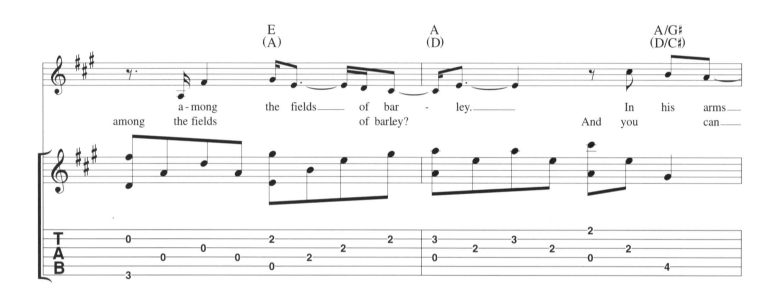

a - mong the fields___ of bar - ley.___ In his arms___
among the fields of barley? And you can___

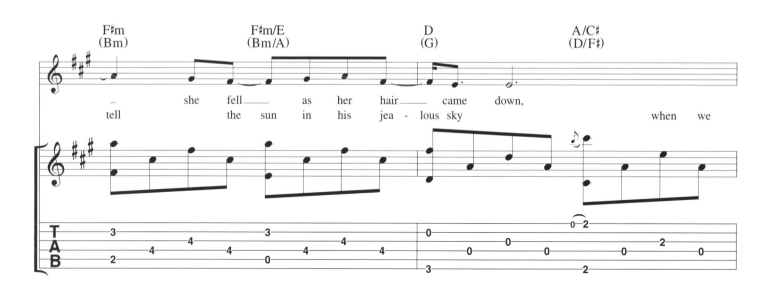

___ she fell___ as her hair___ came down,
tell the sun in his jea - lous sky when we

Bridge

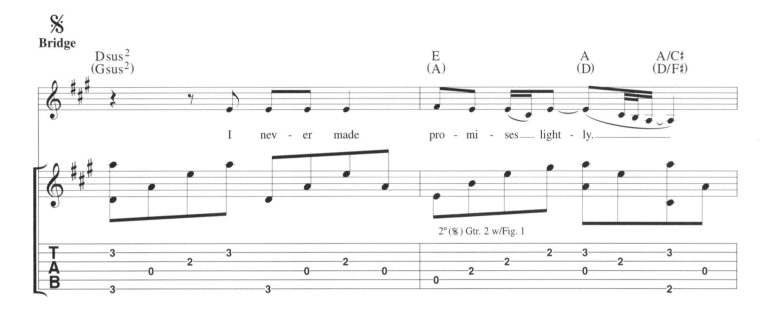

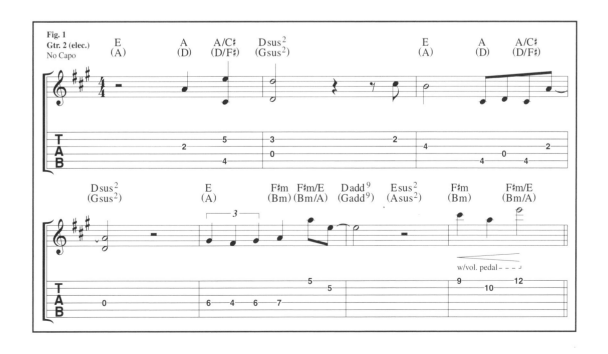

And there have been some that I've bro - ken.

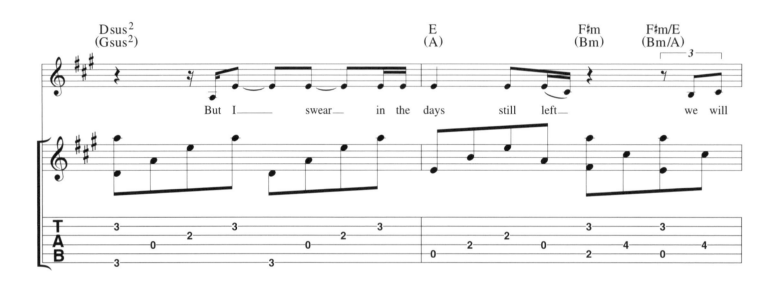

But I swear in the days still left we will

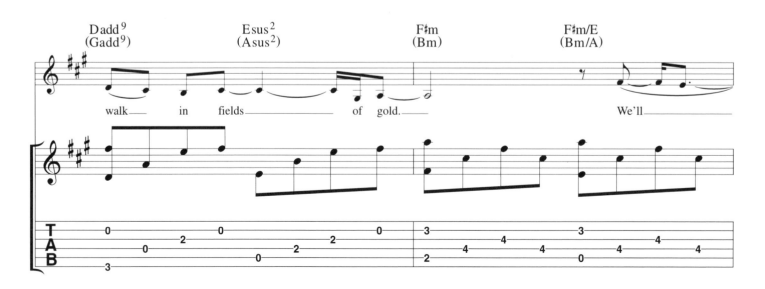

walk in fields of gold. We'll

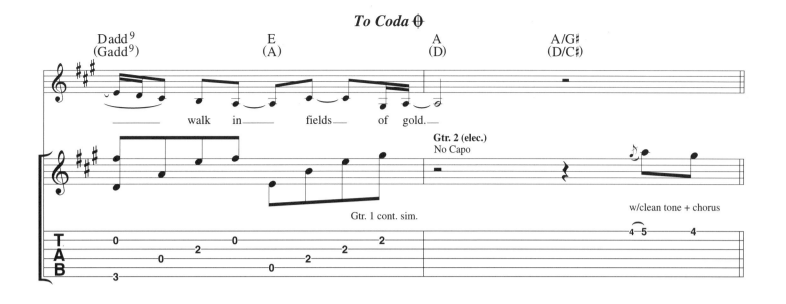

walk in fields of gold.

Solo

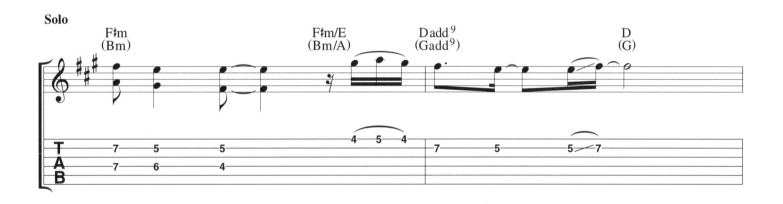

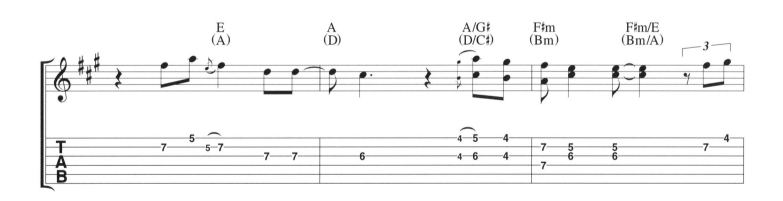

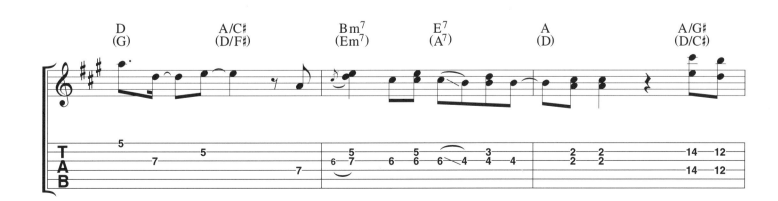

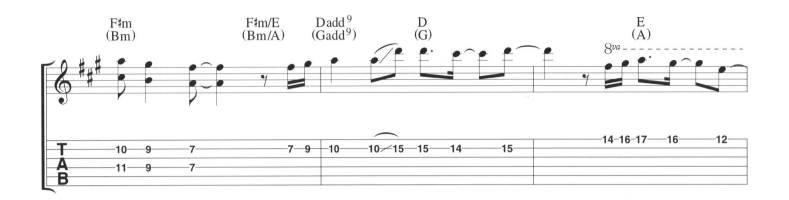

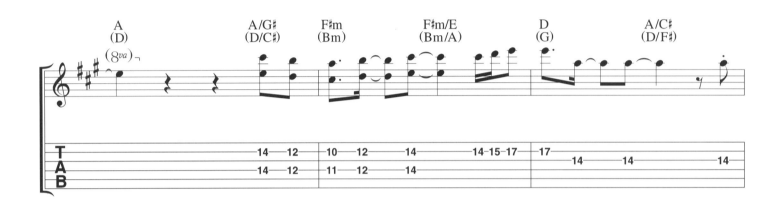

D.%. al Coda

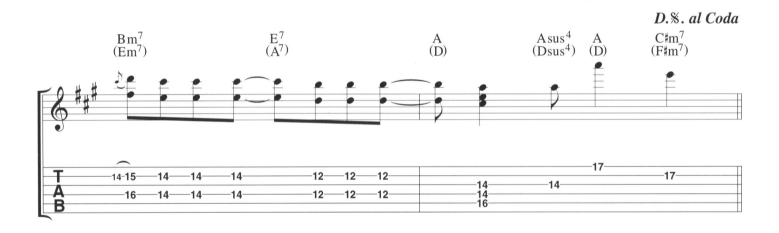

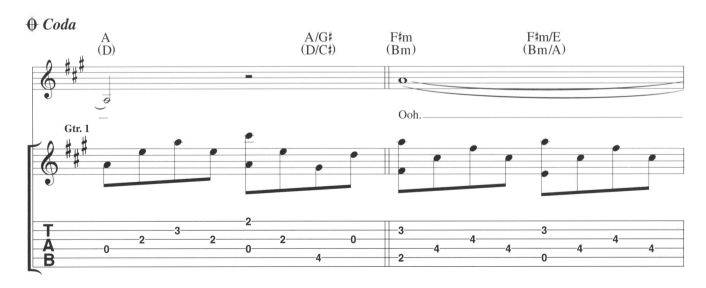

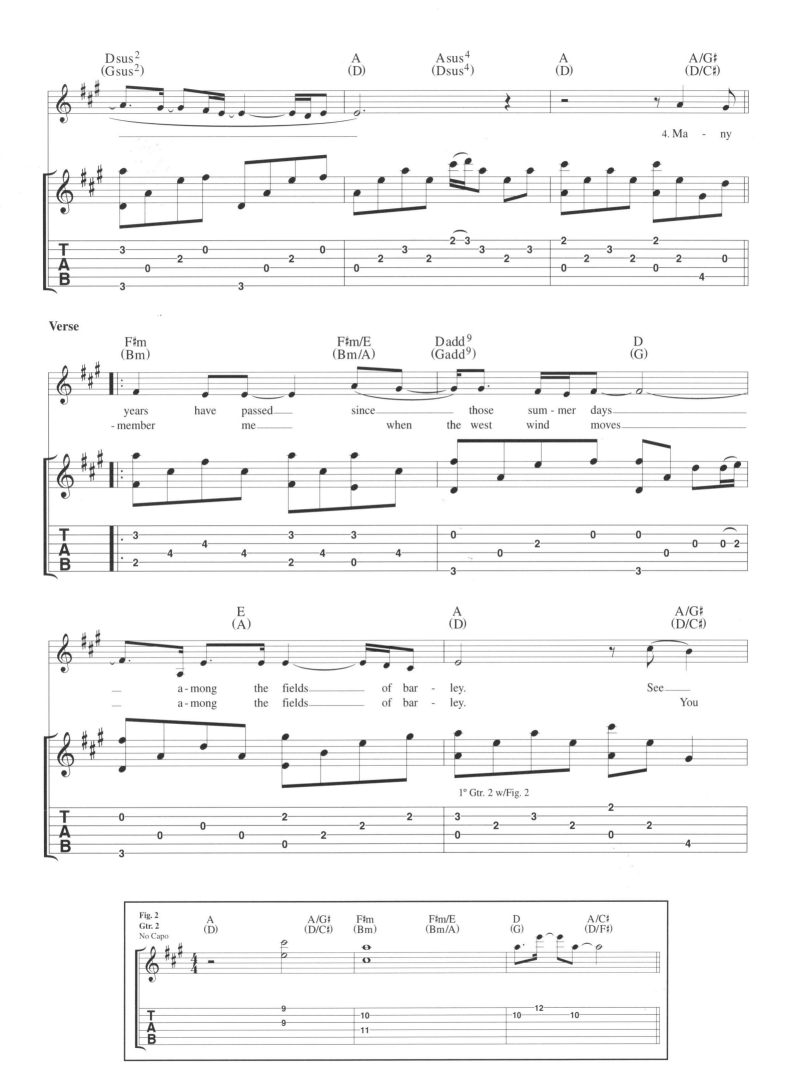

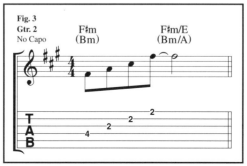

walked__ in__ fields of__ gold.__

rit.

a tempo

Ooh__

Gtr. 2 w/Fig. 4

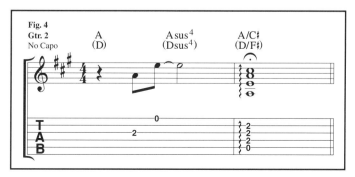

Wade In The Water

Traditional, arranged by Eva Cassidy

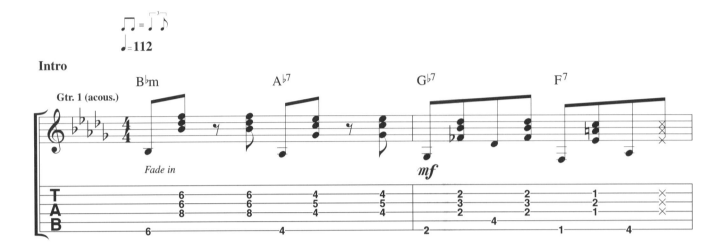

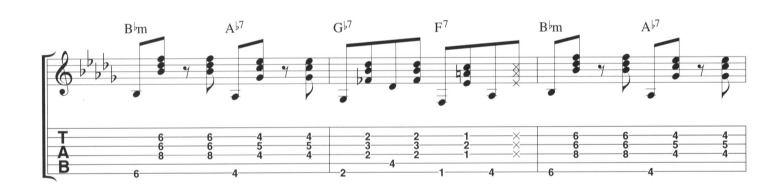

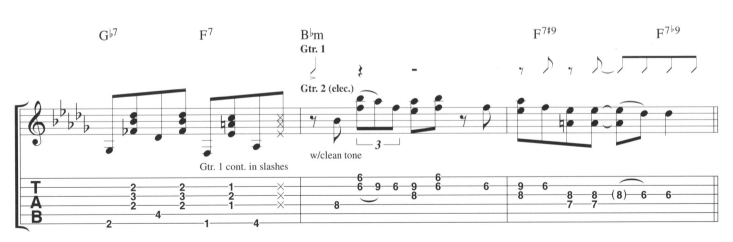

Chorus

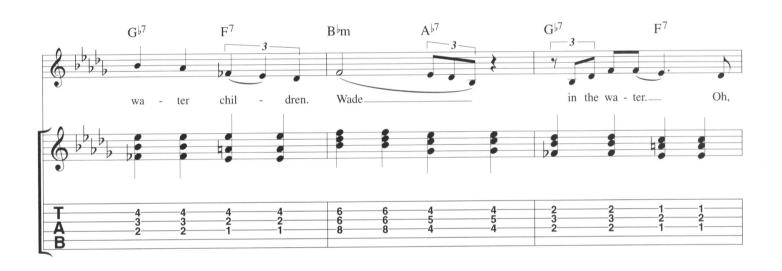

Verse

18

Chorus

Wade___ in the wa - ter.___ Wade___ in the wa - ter chil - dren. Wade_____ in the wa - ter.___ Oh, God's gon - na trou - ble the wa - ter.

Gtr. 2 cont. sim.

Solo

Trumpet arr. for gtr.

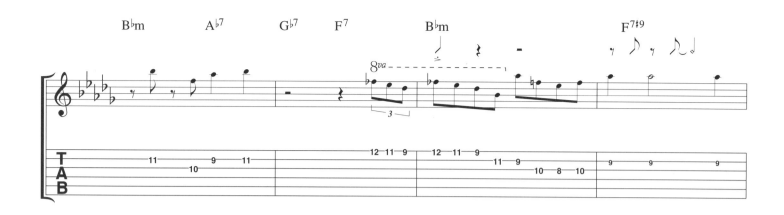

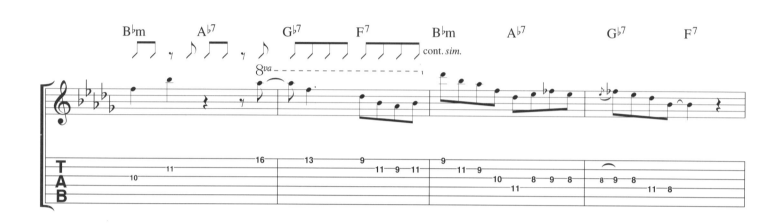

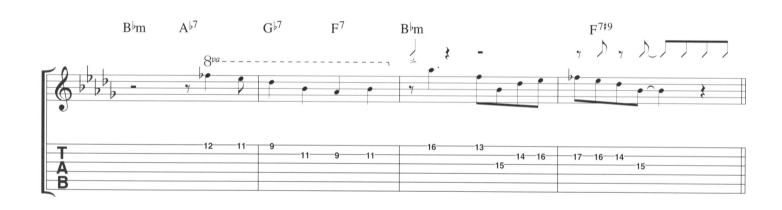

Verse

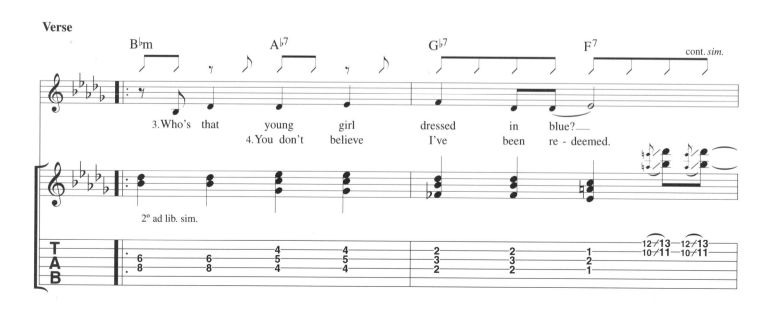

3. Who's that young girl dressed in blue?—
4. You don't believe I've been re-deemed.

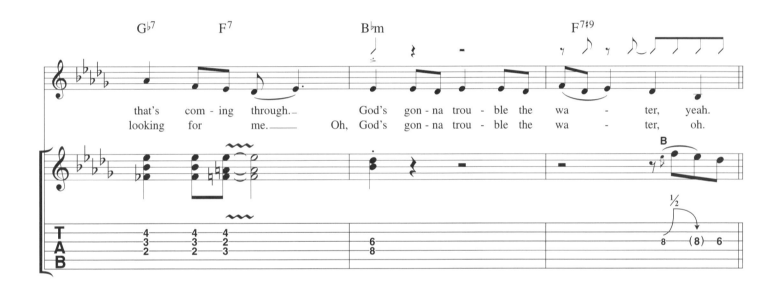

Chorus

21

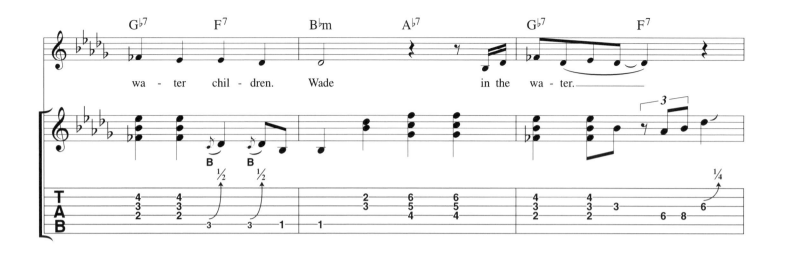

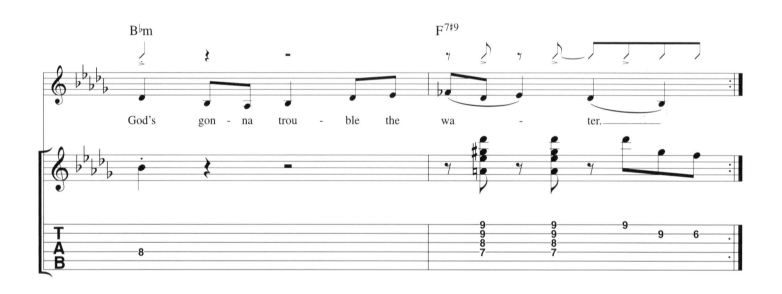

Outro

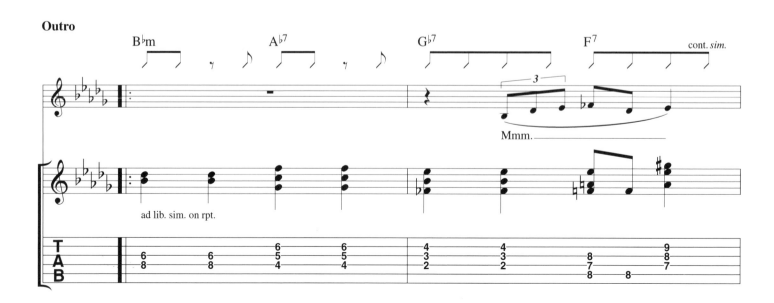

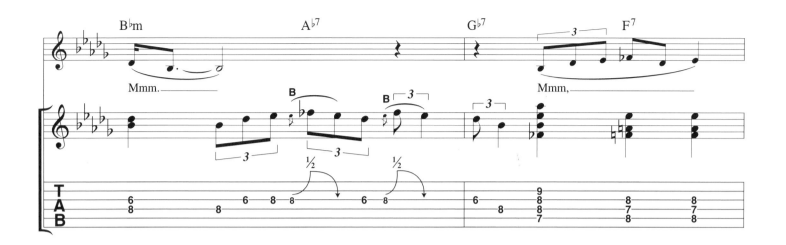

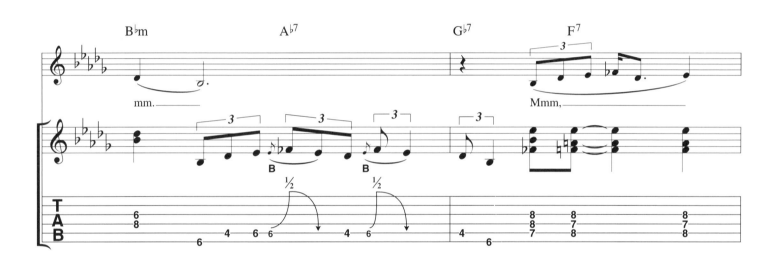

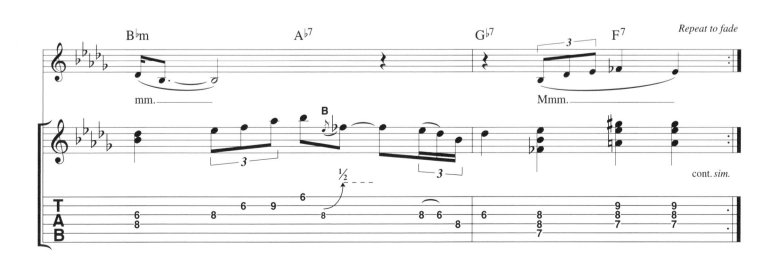

Autumn Leaves

Original Words by Jacques Prevert
Music by Joseph Kosma
English Words by Johnny Mercer

♩ = 75

Intro

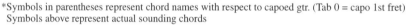

*Symbols in parentheses represent chord names with respect to capoed gtr. (Tab 0 = capo 1st fret)
Symbols above represent actual sounding chords

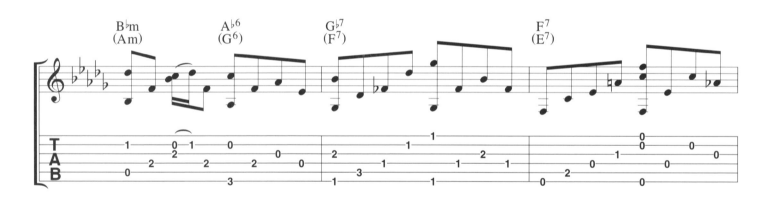

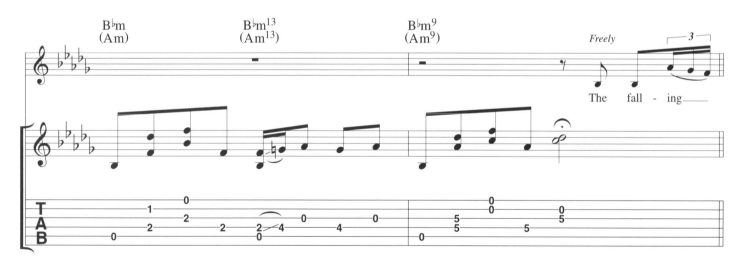

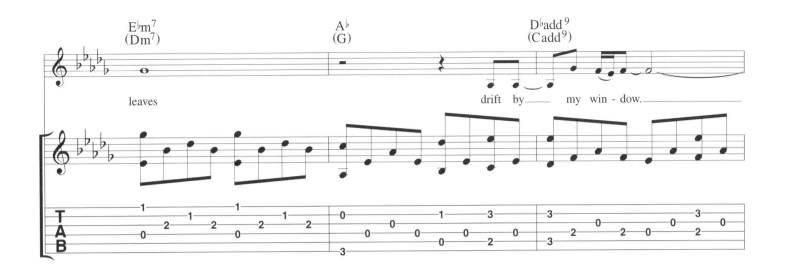

leaves ... drift by___ my win - dow.___

___ The fall - ing___ leaves___ are all___

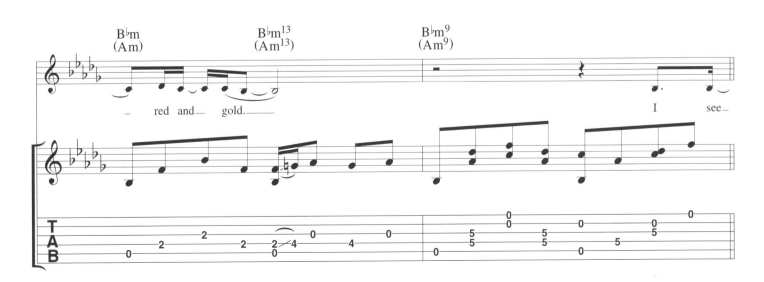

___ red and___ gold.___ I see___

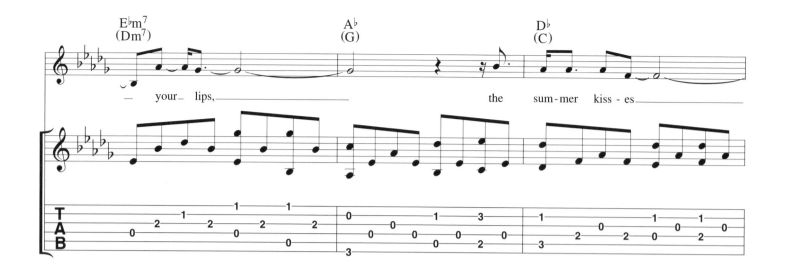

your lips, the sum-mer kiss-es

the sun-burnt hands I

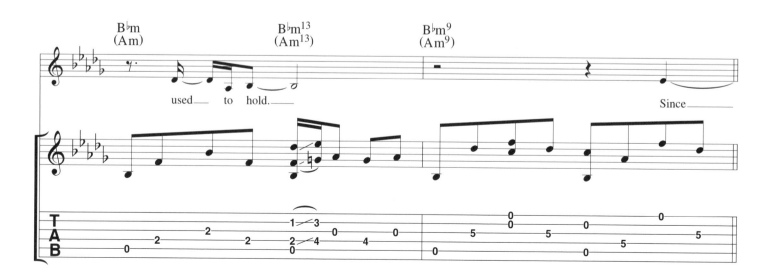

used to hold. Since

26

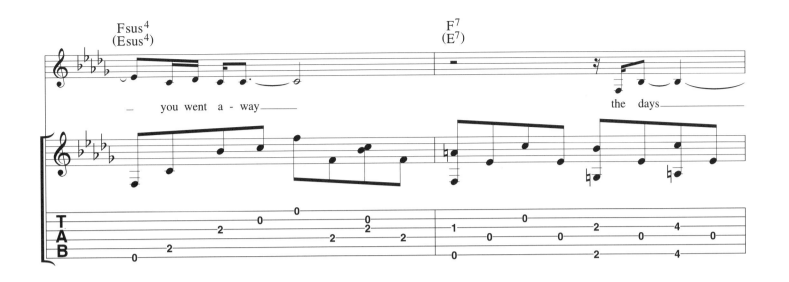

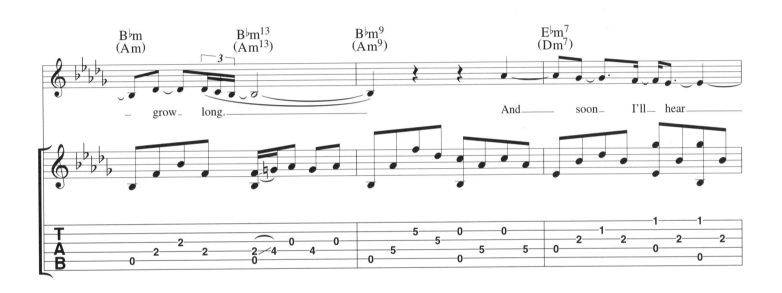

miss you____ most_ of all____ my dar-

-ling,____ when_____ Au-tumn leaves____ start_

____ to fall.____

Solo

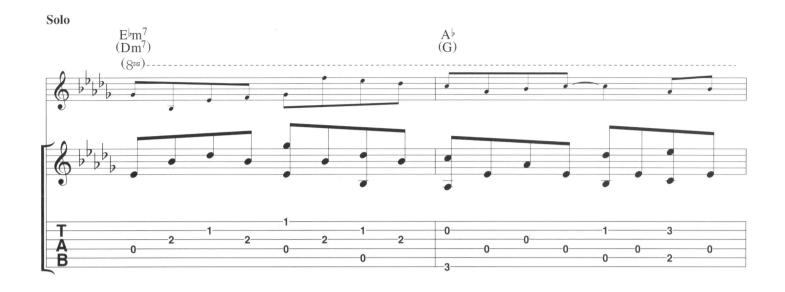

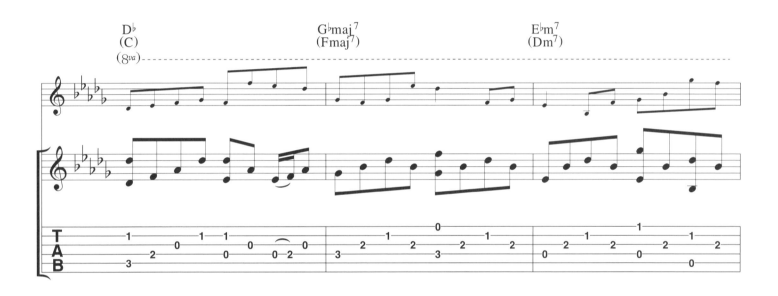

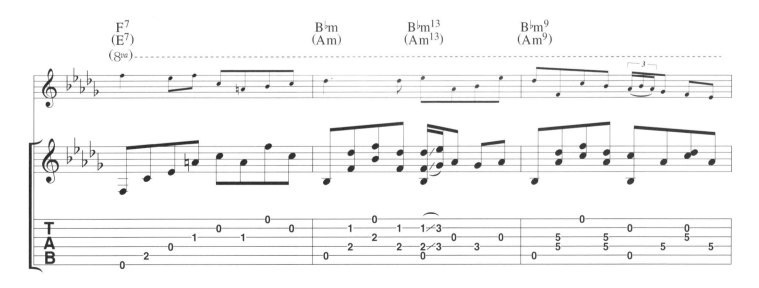

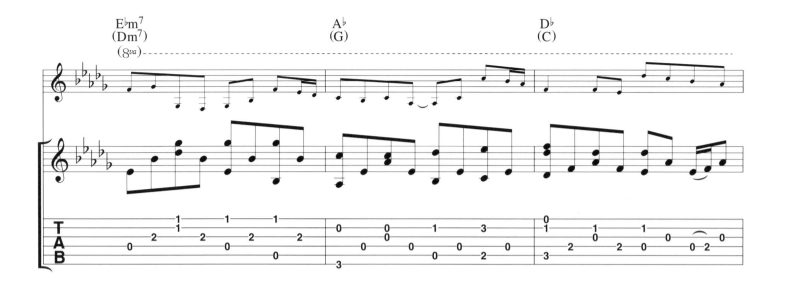

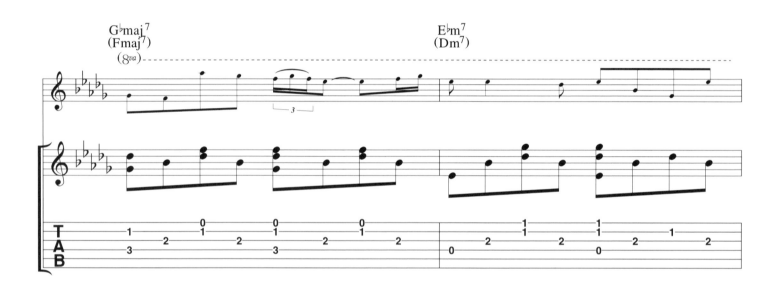

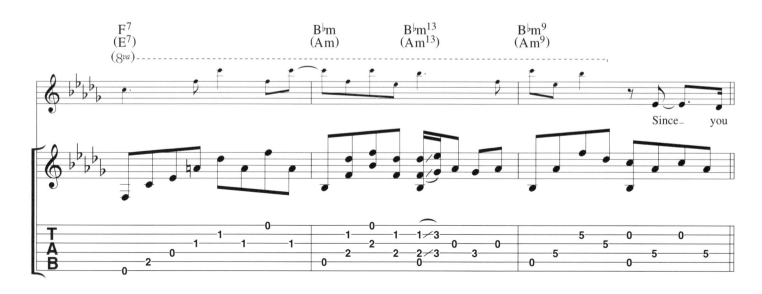

Since you

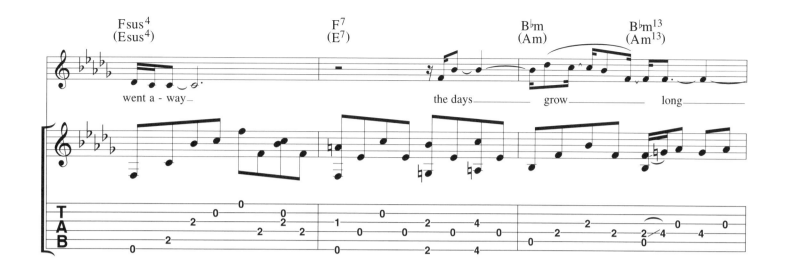

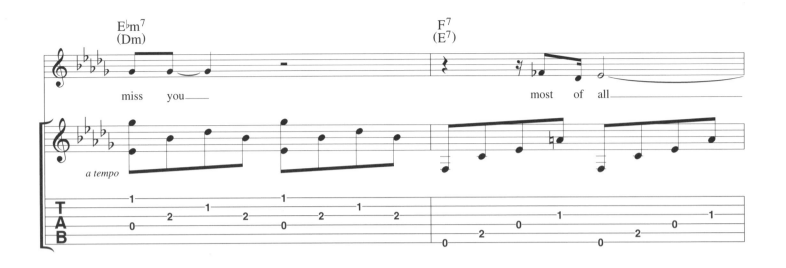

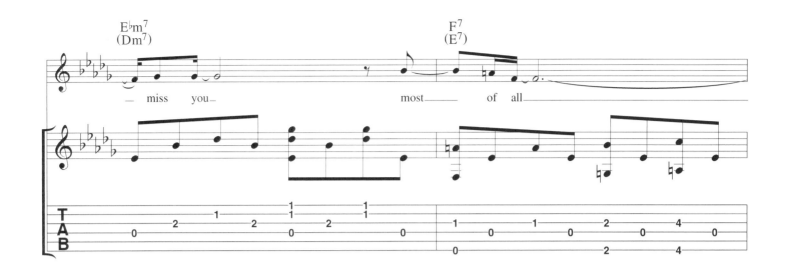

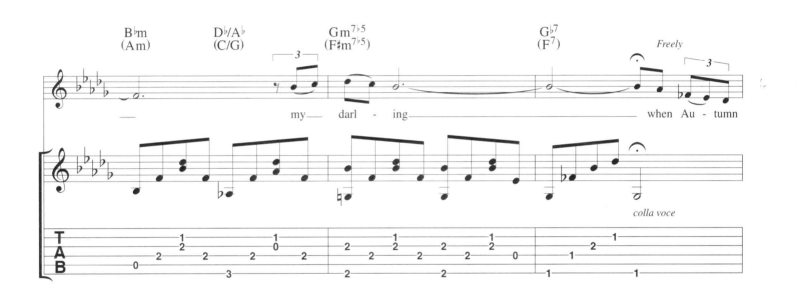

Wayfaring Stranger

Traditional, arranged by Eva Cassidy

† Gtr. 1 notated w/up stems, Gtr. 2 notated w/down stems in cue notes.

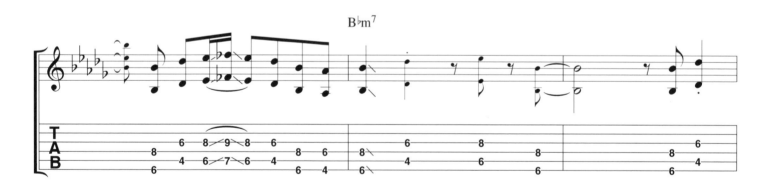

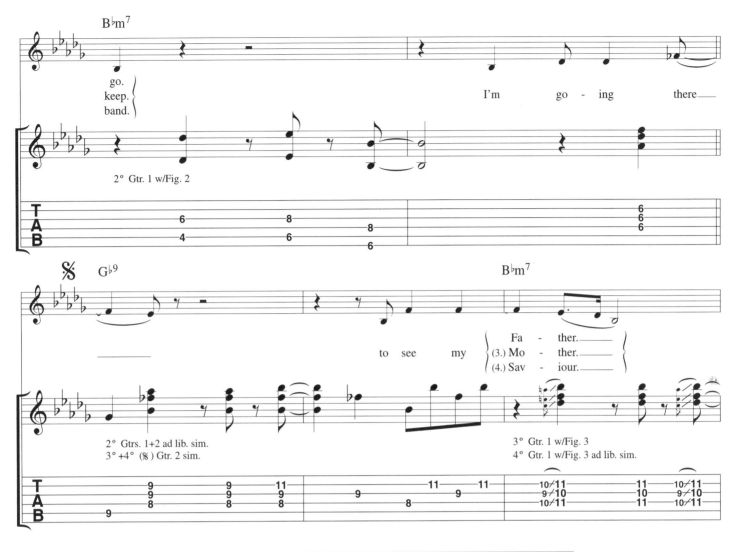

go.
keep.
band.

I'm go - ing there___

2° Gtr. 1 w/Fig. 2

to see my

(3.) Mo - ther.___
(4.) Sav - iour.___

Fa - ther.___

2° Gtrs. 1+2 ad lib. sim.
3° +4° (𝄋) Gtr. 2 sim.

3° Gtr. 1 w/Fig. 3
4° Gtr. 1 w/Fig. 3 ad lib. sim.

Fig. 2
Gtr. 2

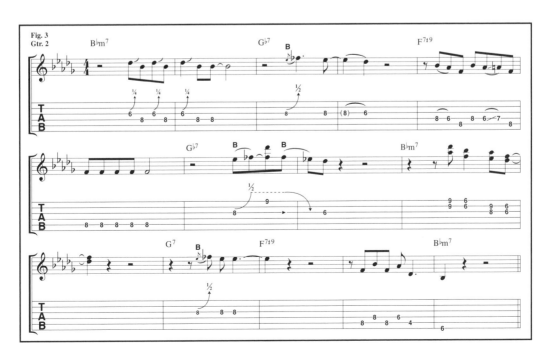

Fig. 3
Gtr. 2

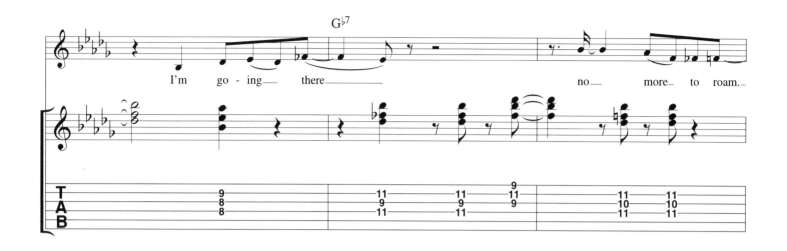

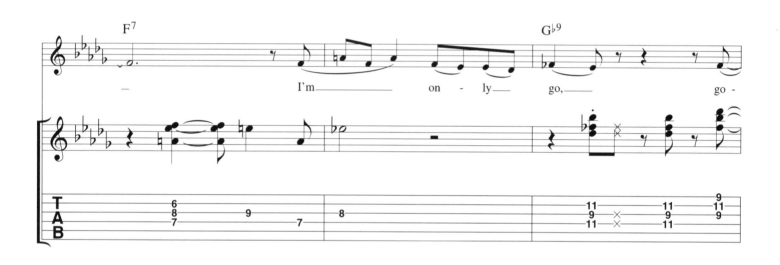

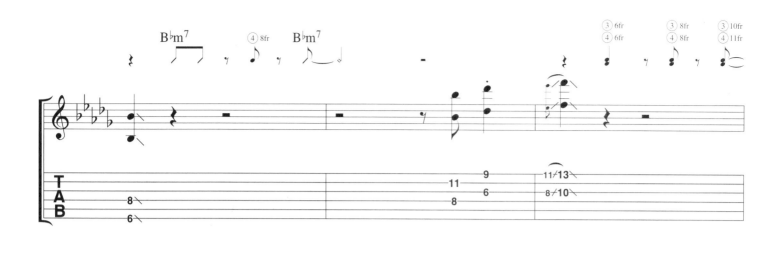

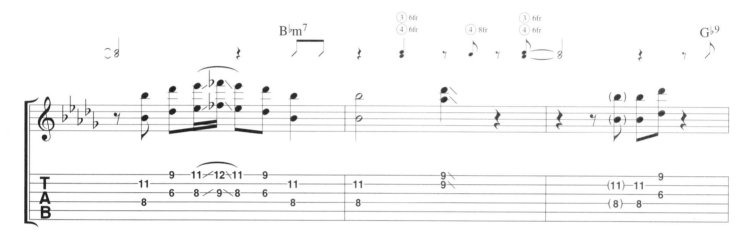

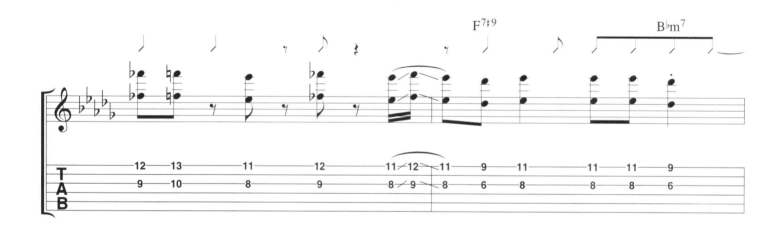

D.%. al Coda
(w/repeat)

I'm go-ing there

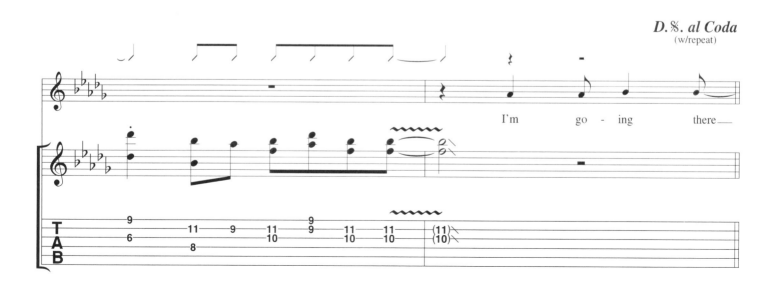

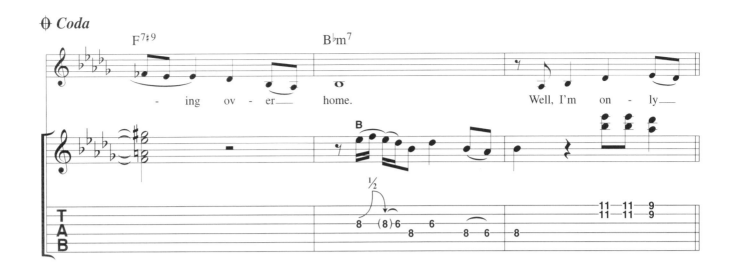

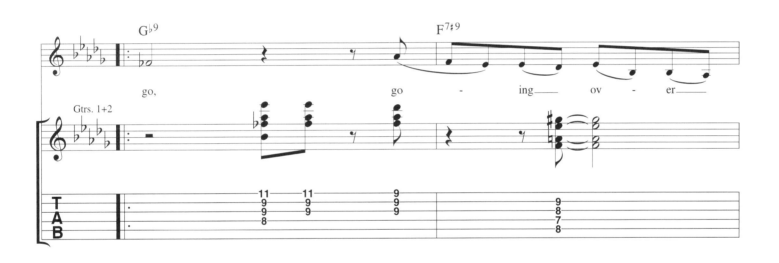

Time Is A Healer

Words & Music by Diane Scanlon & Greg Smith

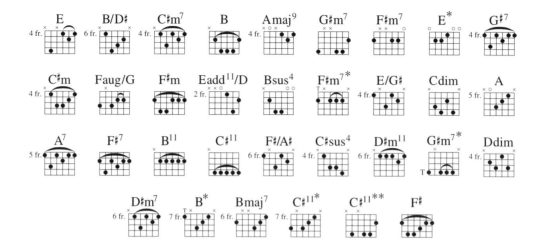

Intro

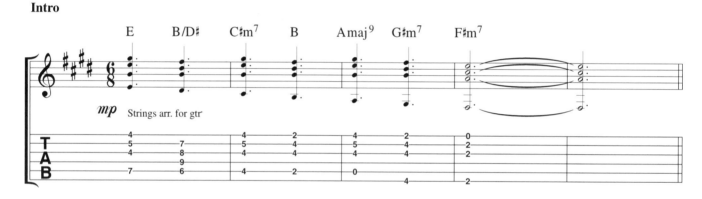

Verse

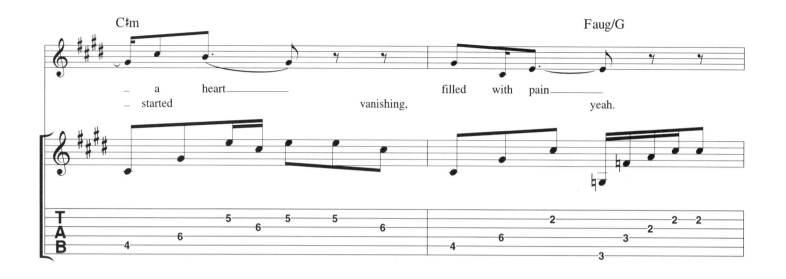

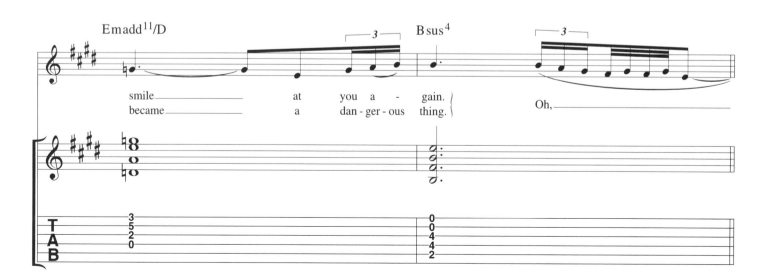

Chorus

if time is a heal - er,_____ mm,____ mm,

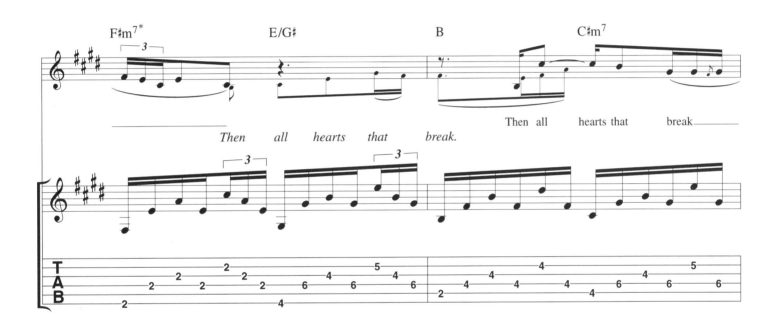

_____ Then all hearts that break.

Then all hearts that break_____

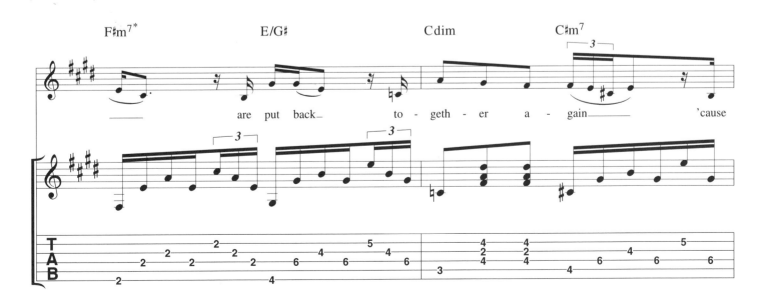

_____ are put back____ to - geth - er a - gain_____ 'cause

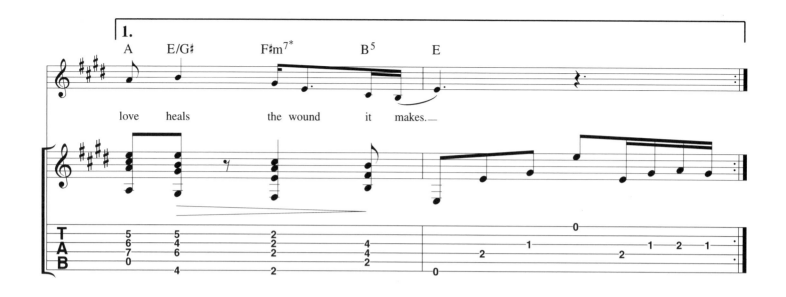

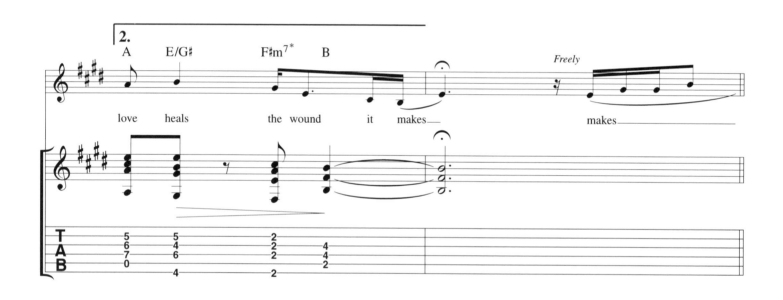

Bridge

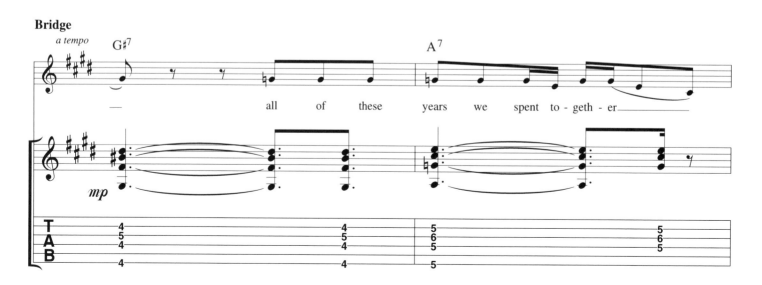

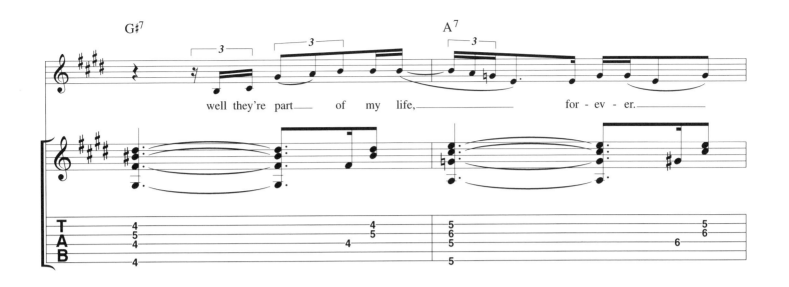

well they're part___ of my life,_____ for - ev - er._____

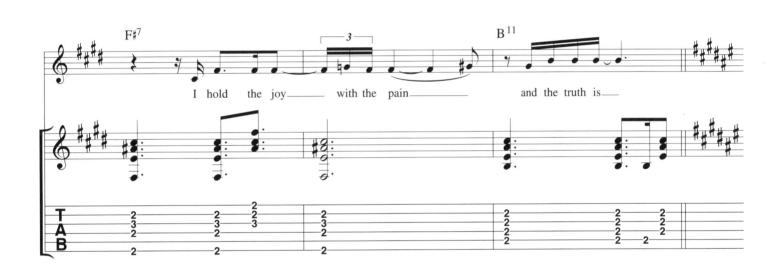

I hold the joy___ with the pain_____ and the truth is___

I miss you___ my friend._____

let ring

mf

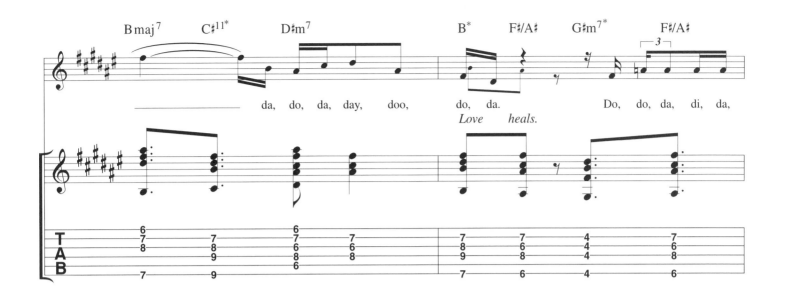

da, do, da, day, doo, do, da. Do, do, da, di, da,

Love heals.

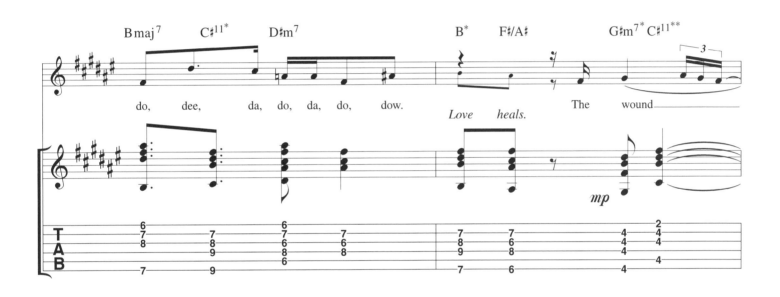

do, dee, da, do, da, do, dow. The wound

Love heals.

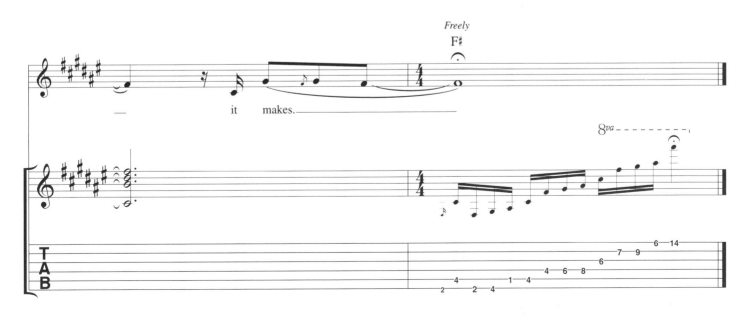

it makes.

Songbird

Words & Music by Christine McVie

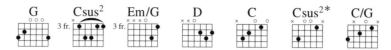

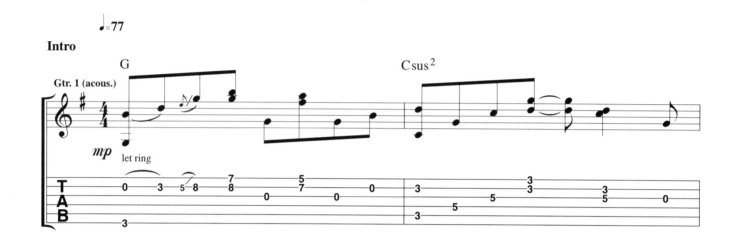

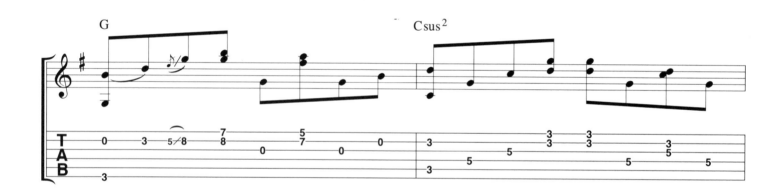

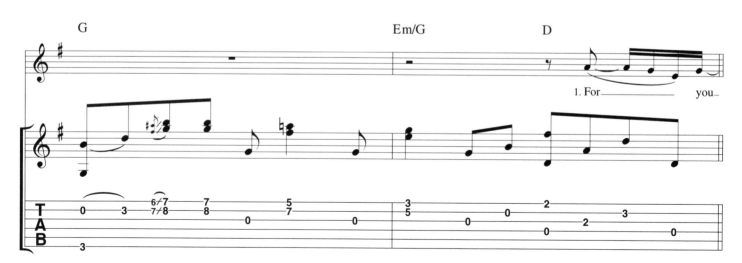

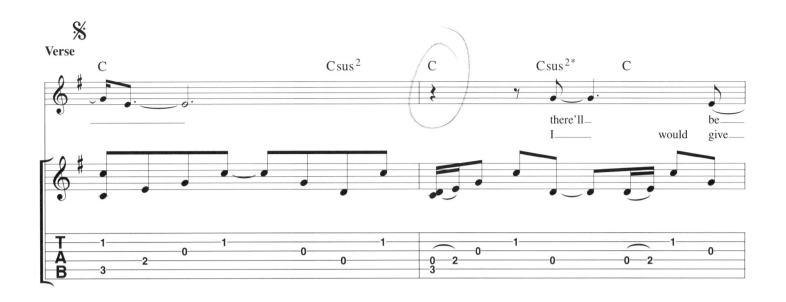

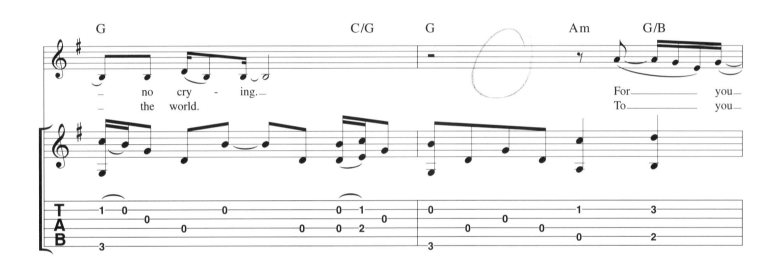

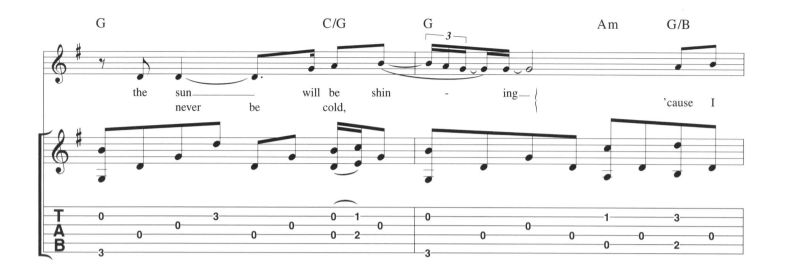

the sun____ will be shin - - ing____ {
never be cold,   'cause I

feel   that when___ I'm   with you   it's al -

- right,_____   I   know__

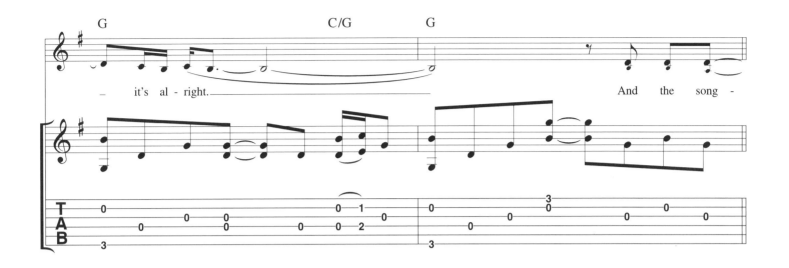

Chorus

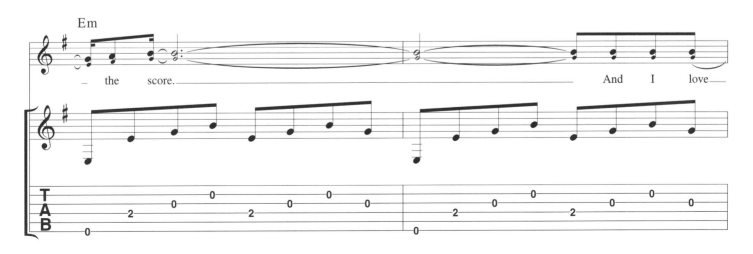

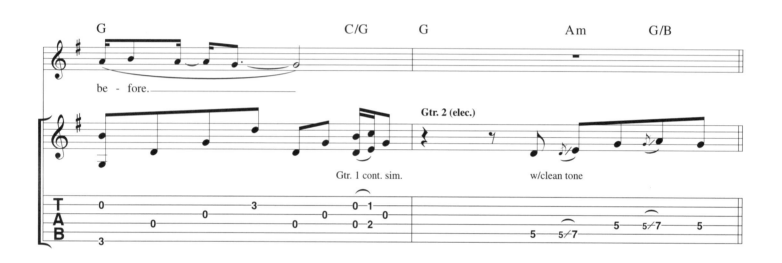

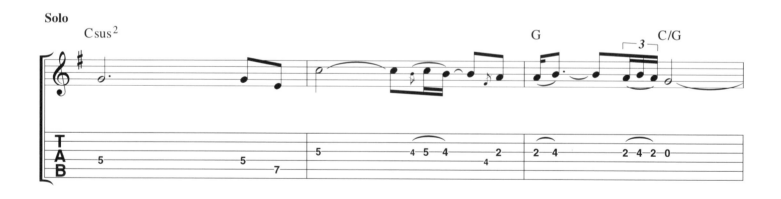

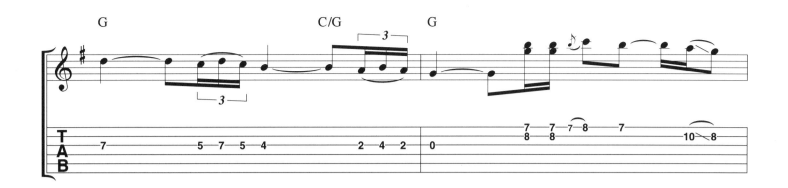

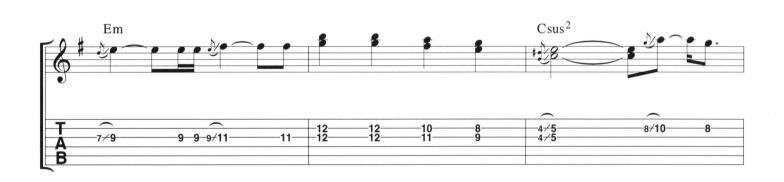

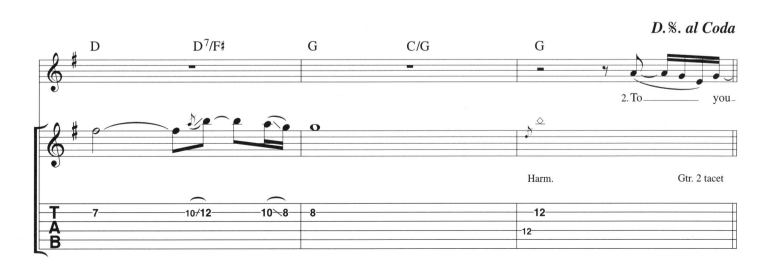

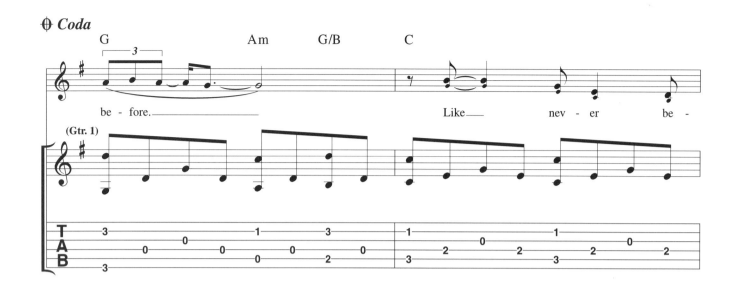

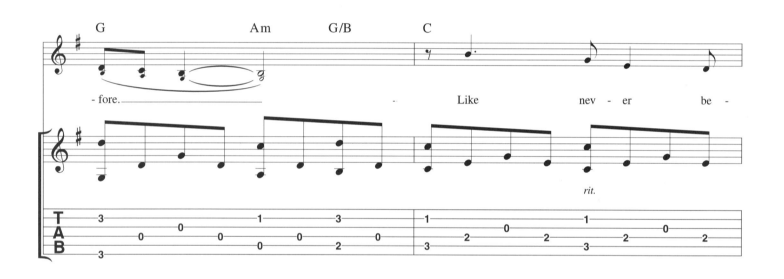

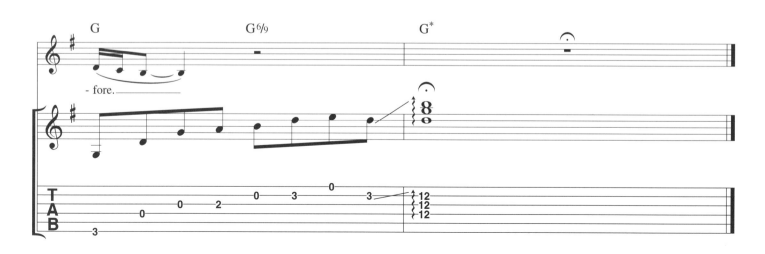

56

People Get Ready

Words & Music by Curtis Mayfield

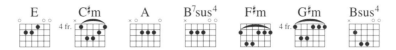

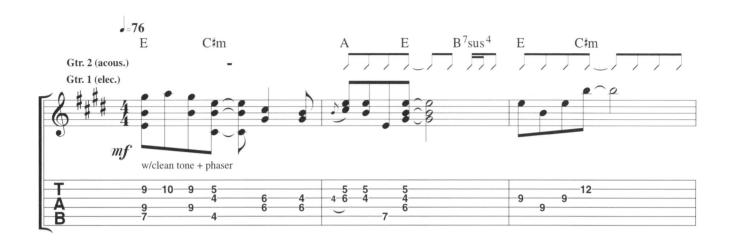

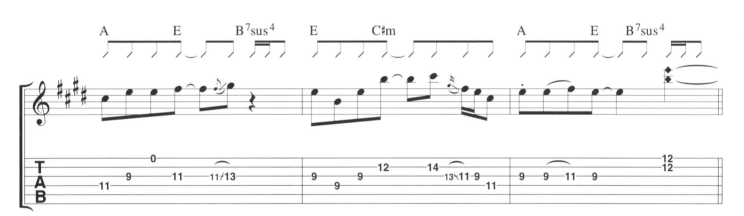

1. Peo - ple get rea - dy____ there's a train a - com - ing.
2. Peo - ple get rea - dy for the train to Jord - an.
(Verse 3 (%) see block lyric)

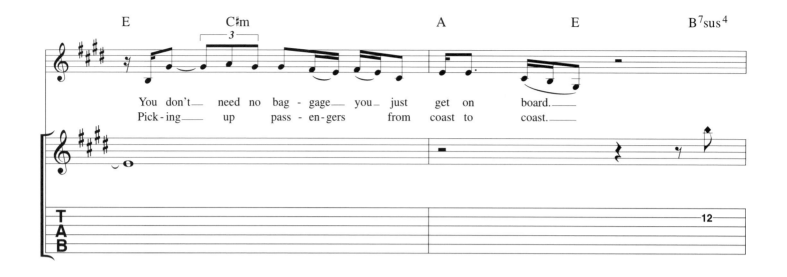

You don't___ need no bag - gage___ you___ just get on board.___
Pick - ing___ up pass - en - gers from coast to coast.___

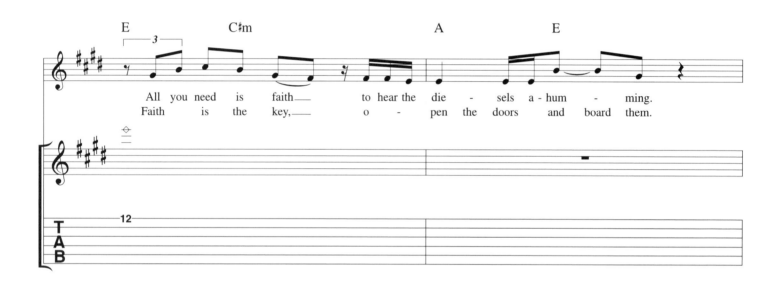

All you need is faith___ to hear the die - sels a - hum - ming.
Faith is the key,___ o - pen the doors and board them.

To Coda ⊕

You don't need no tick - et___ you___ just thank___ the Lord.___ Yeah,___
There's room for all of the love___ and honesty.___

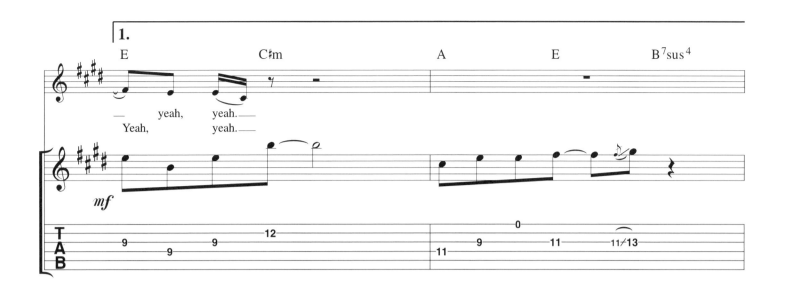

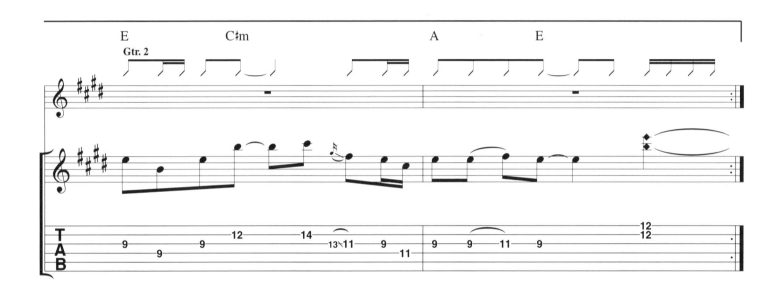

Solo

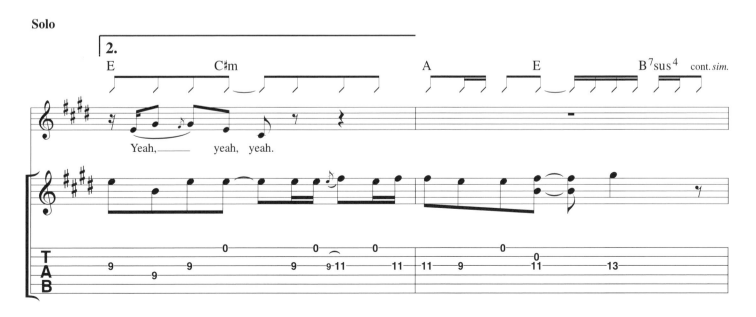

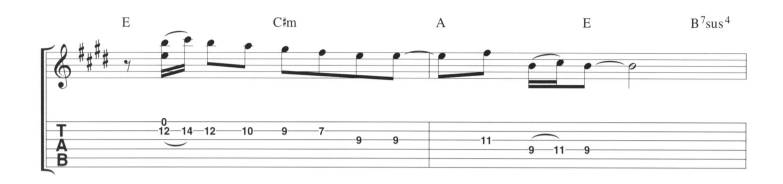

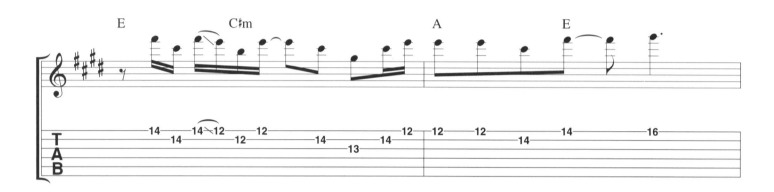

D.𝄋. al Coda

3. Now

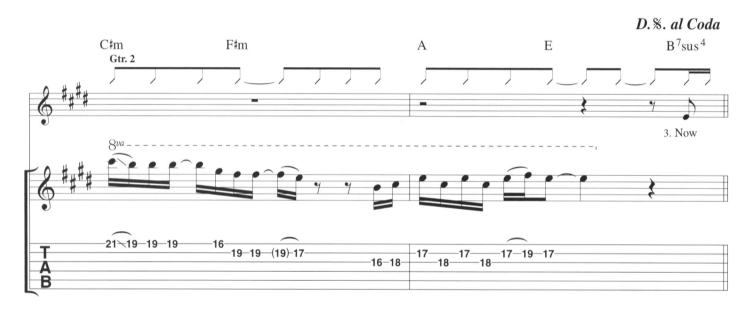

Ⓞ *Coda*

— Peo - ple get rea - dy there's a train — a-com ing.—

You don't— need no bag-gage you—————— just get on——— board. All you need

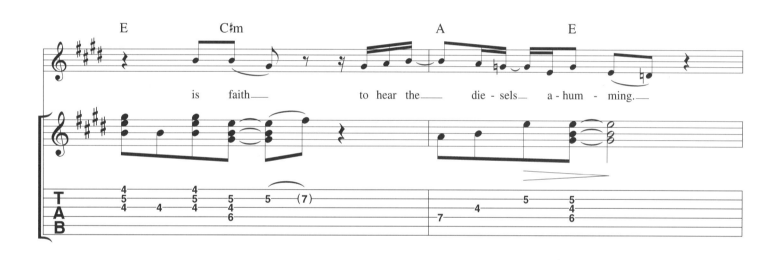

is faith——— to hear the— die-sels— a-hum - ming.—

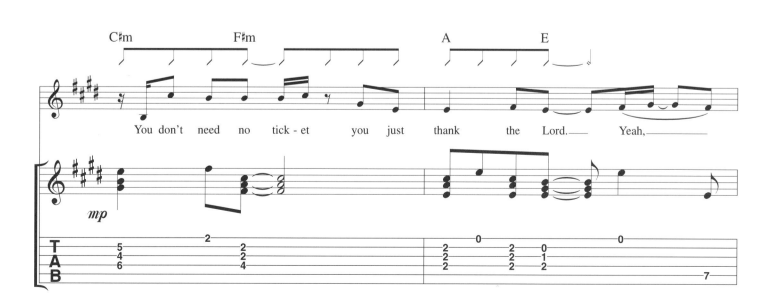

You don't need no tick-et you just thank the Lord.— Yeah,————

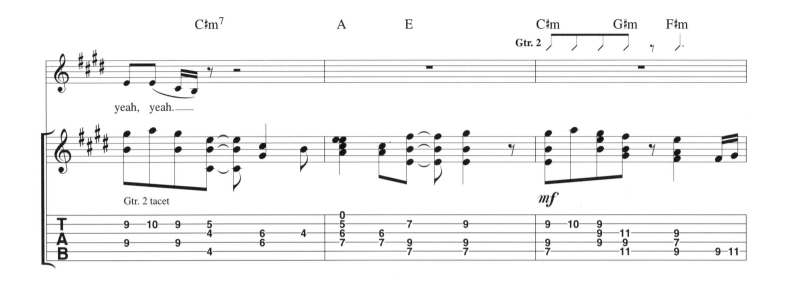

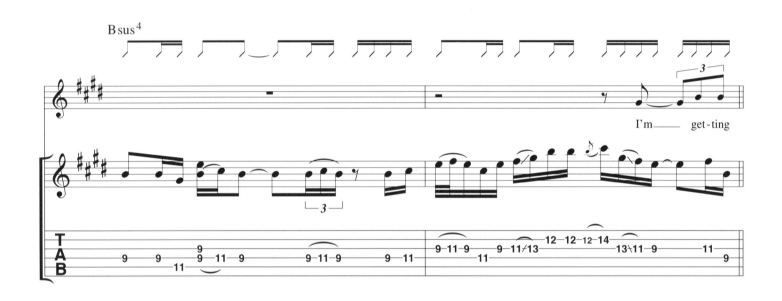

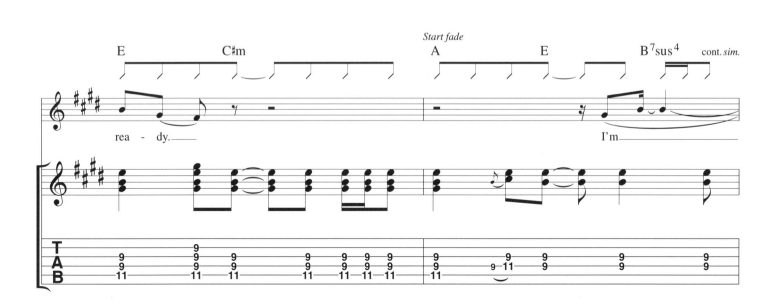

Verse 3:

Now there ain't no room for the hopeless sinner
Who's hard on mankind just to save his own
Have pity on those whose chances are thinner
'Cause there's no hiding place from the king on his throne.

I Know You By Heart

Words & Music by Diane Scanlon & Eve Nelson

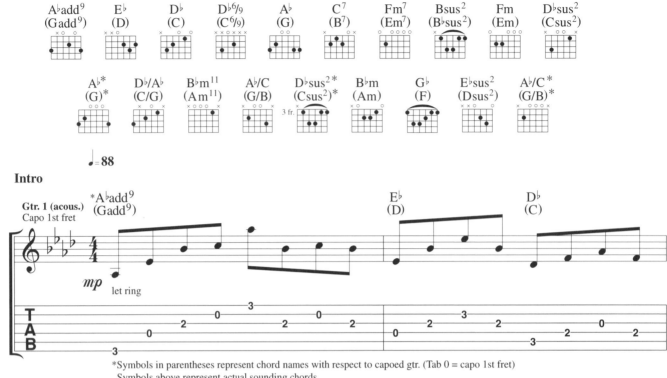

*Symbols in parentheses represent chord names with respect to capoed gtr. (Tab 0 = capo 1st fret)
Symbols above represent actual sounding chords

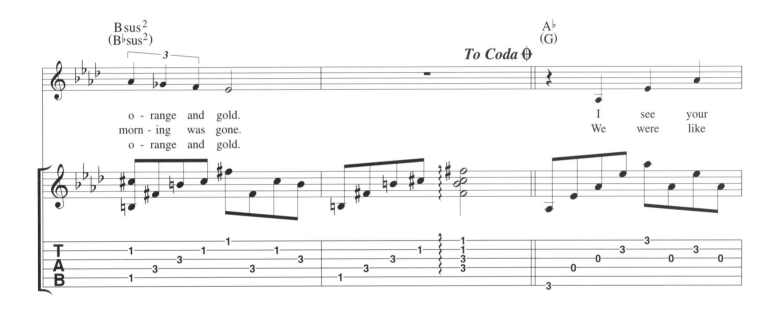

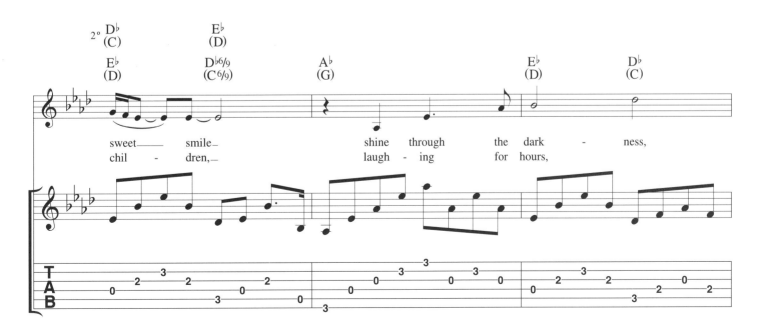

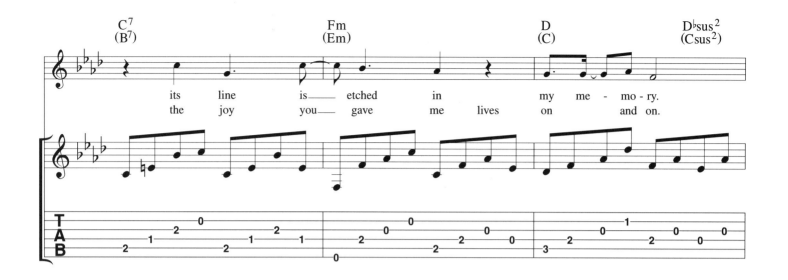

its   line   is   etched   in   my me - mo - ry.
the   joy   is   you   gave   me lives   on   and on.

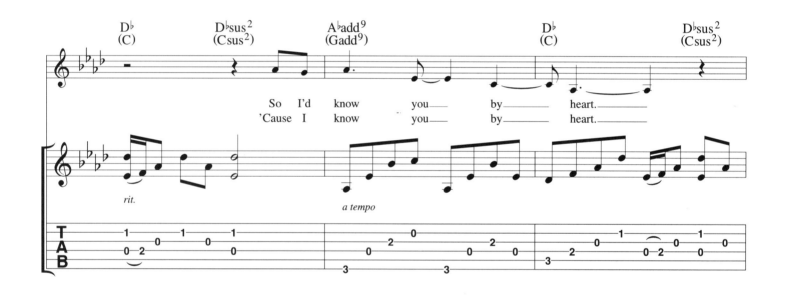

So   I'd   know   you   by   heart.
'Cause I   know   you   by   heart.

rit.   *a tempo*

1.

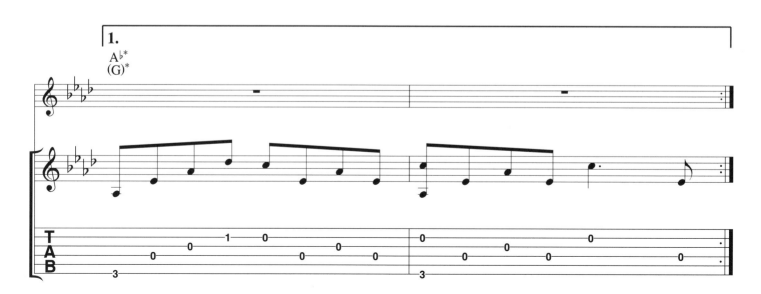

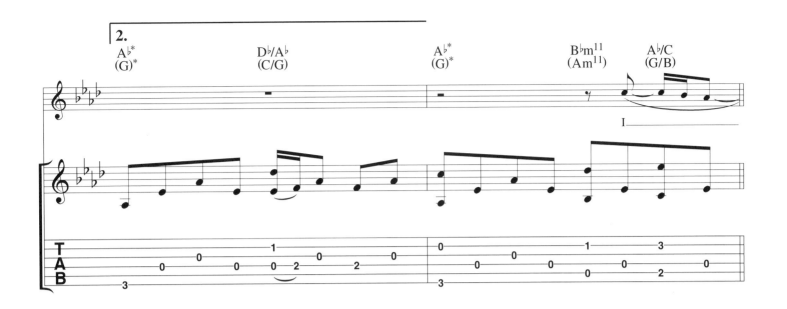

Bridge

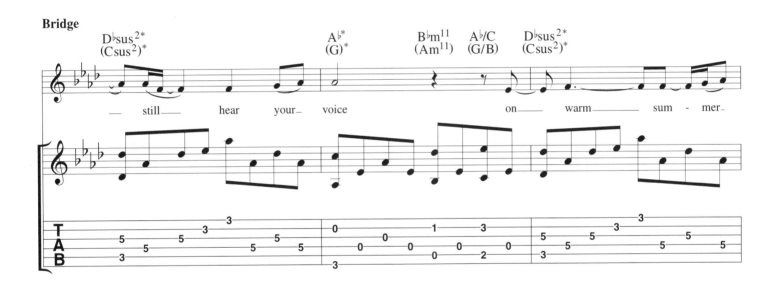

still hear your voice on warm sum - mer

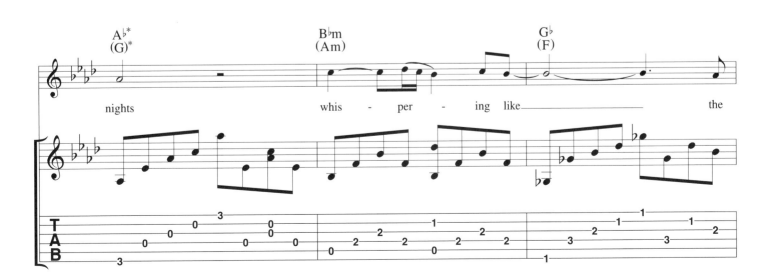

nights whis - per - ing like the

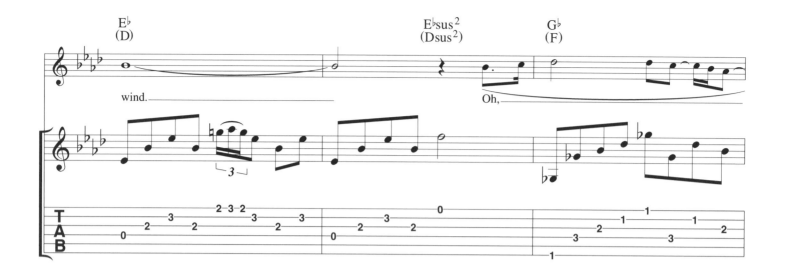

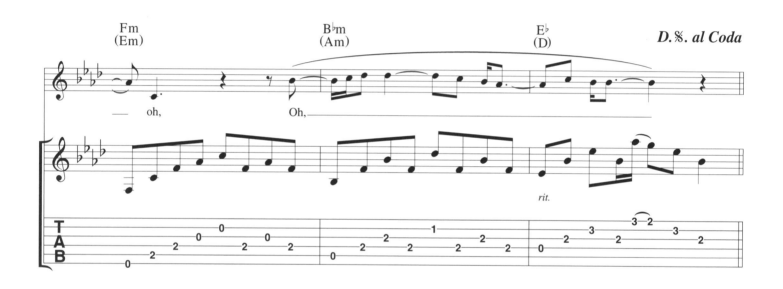

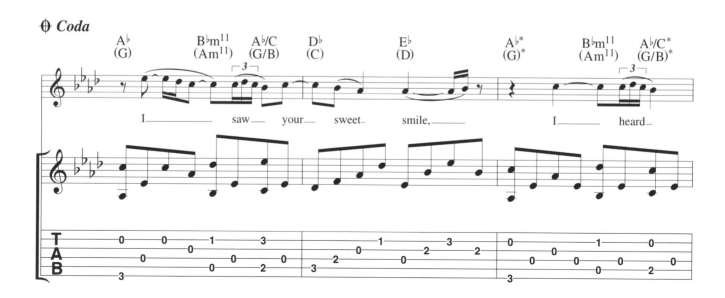

Oh, Had I A Golden Thread

Words & Music by Pete Seeger

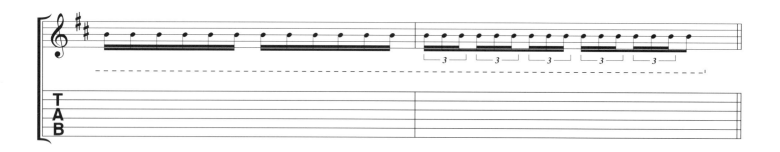

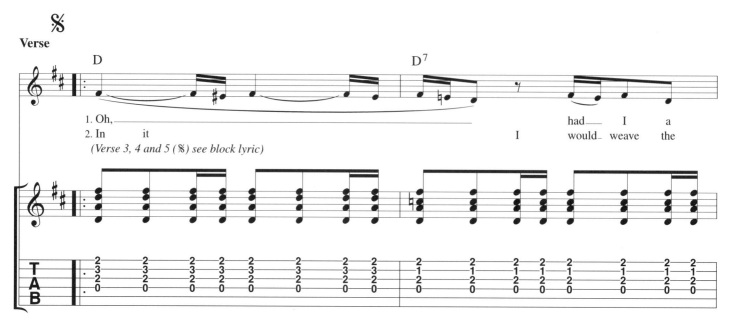

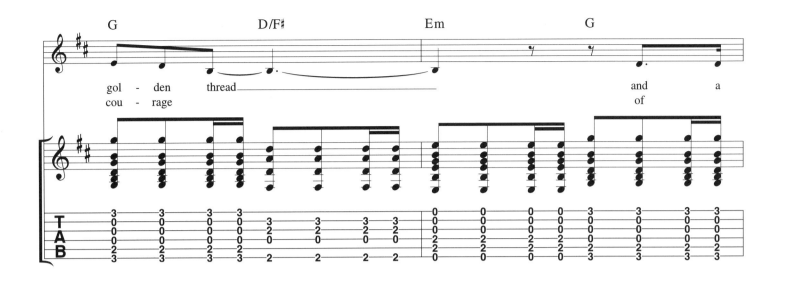

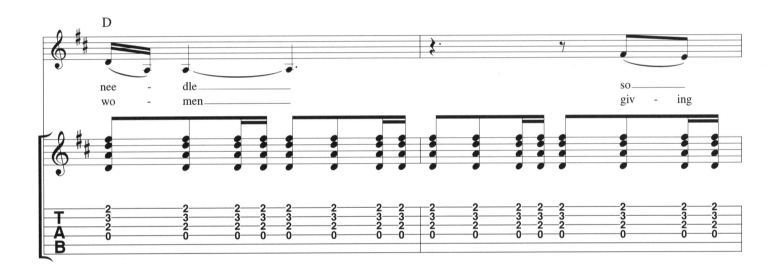

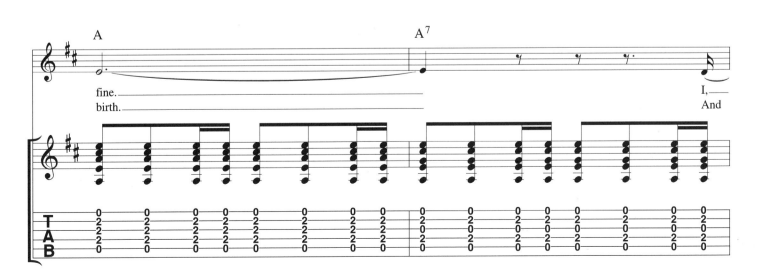

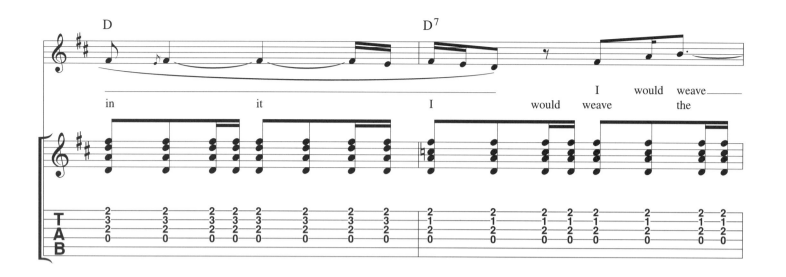

in   it   I   would   weave   would weave the

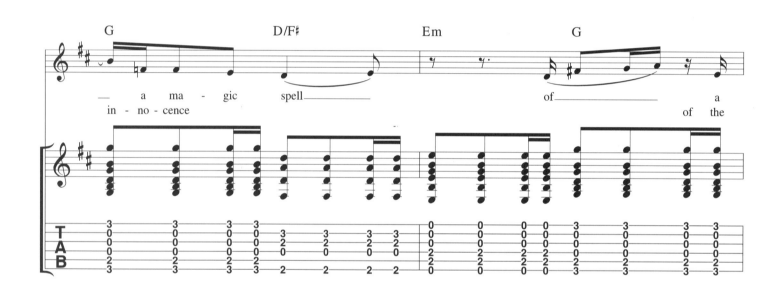

— a ma - gic   spell   of   a
in - no - cence   of the

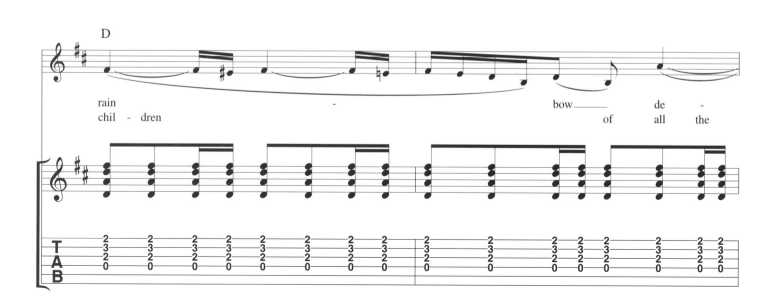

rain   -   bow   de -
chil - dren   of all the

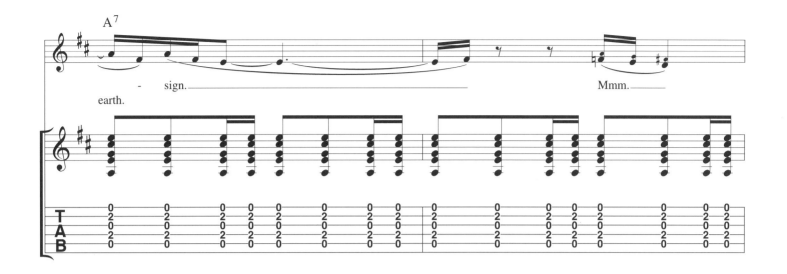

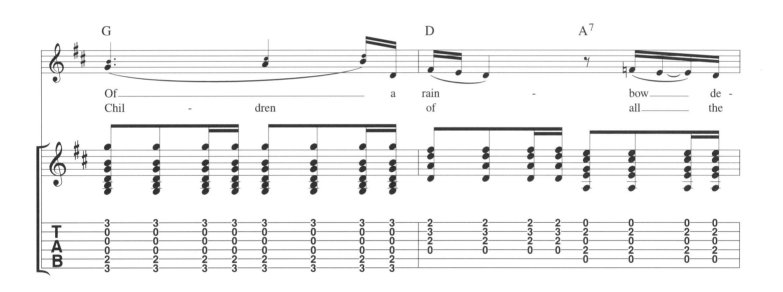

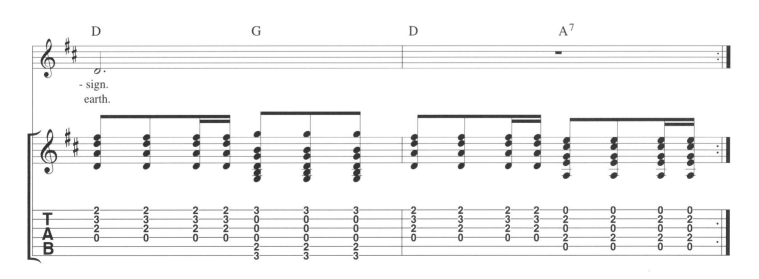

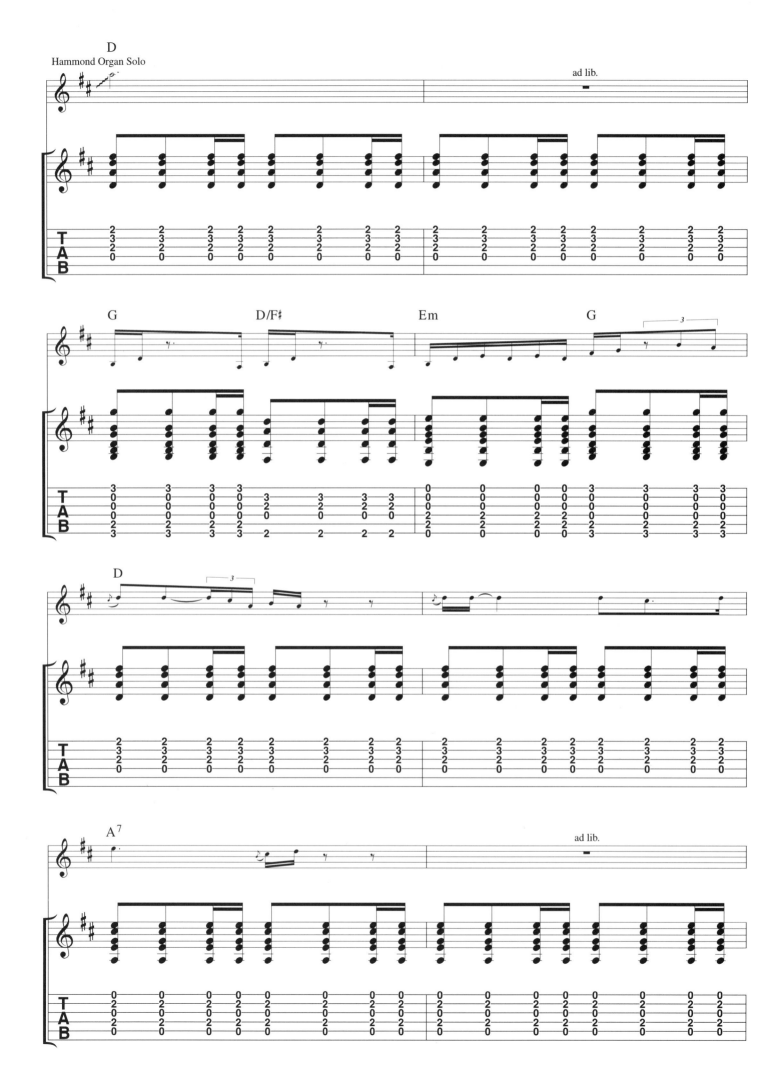

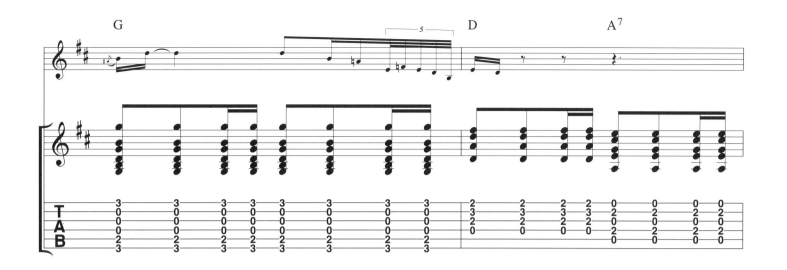

D.%.
repeat verse to fade

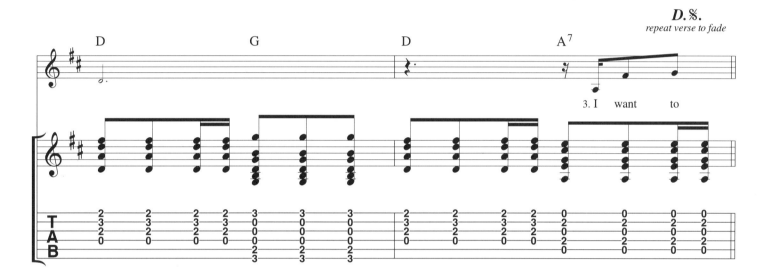

3. I want to

Verse 3:

I want to show my brothers and sisters my rainbow design
'Cause I would bind up this sorry world
With my hand and my heart and mind
Oh, hand and heart and mind.

Verse 4:

Oh, had I a golden thread and a needle so fine
I would weave a magic spell
Of a rainbow design
Of a rainbow design.

Verse 5:

- Ad lib. to fade.

Over The Rainbow

Words by E.Y. Harburg

Music by Harold Arlen

*Symbols in parentheses represent chord names with respect to capoed gtr. (Tab 0 = capo 1st fret)
Symbols above represent actual sounding chords

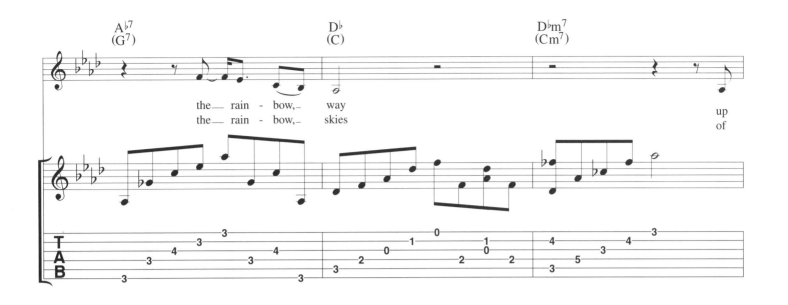

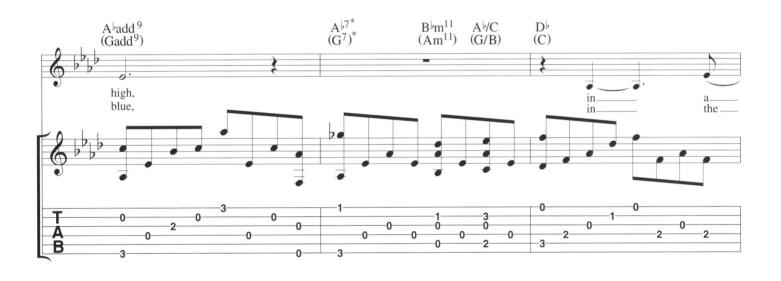

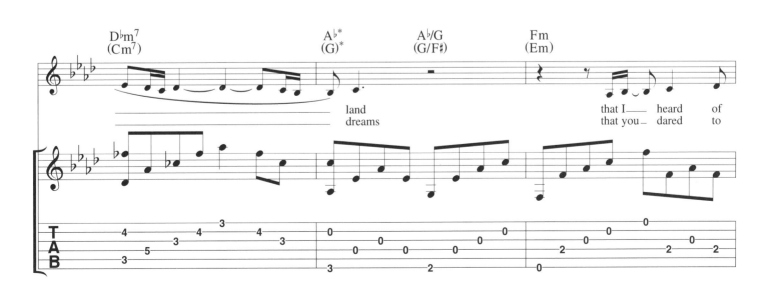

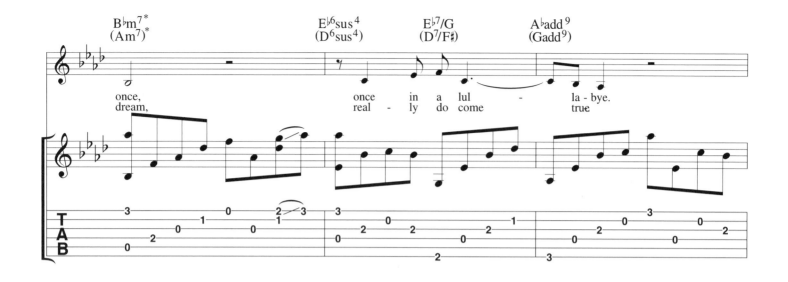

once,
dream,

once in a lul - la - bye.
real - ly do come true

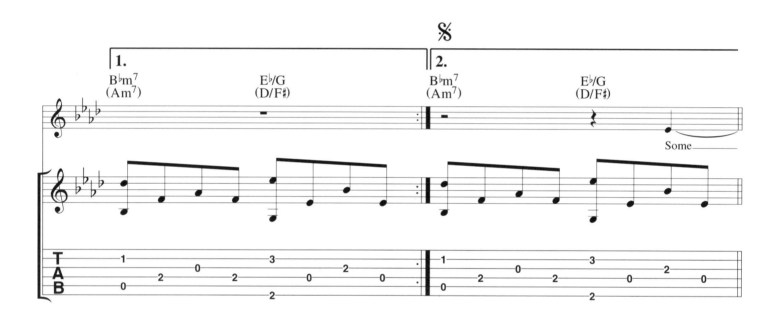

1.

2.

Some

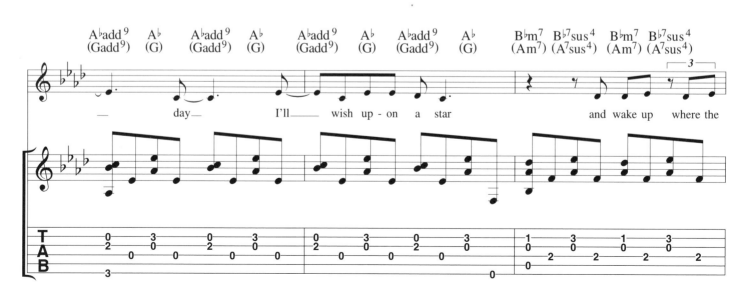

day I'll wish up - on a star and wake up where the

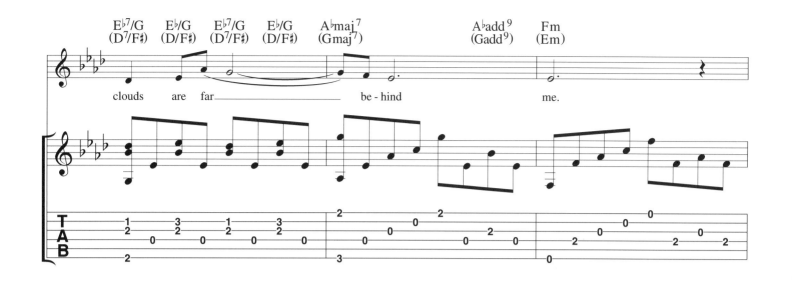

clouds   are   far_____   be - hind   me.

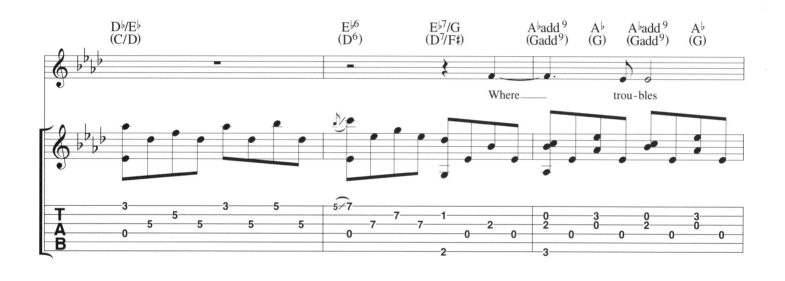

Where_____   trou - bles

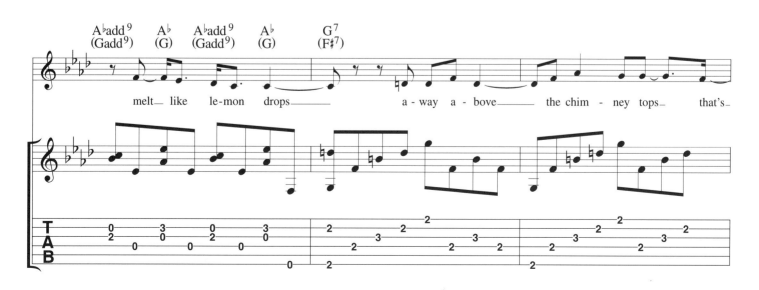

melt___ like   le - mon   drops_____   a - way   a - bove_____   the   chim - ney   tops___   that's

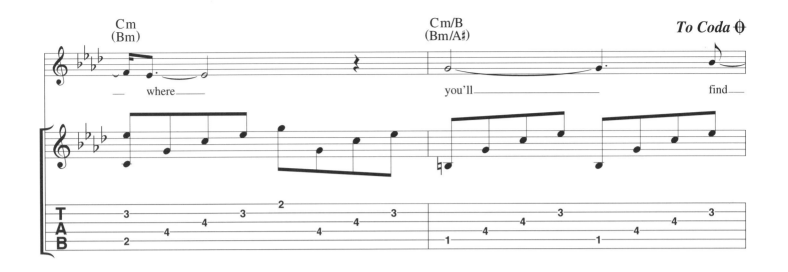

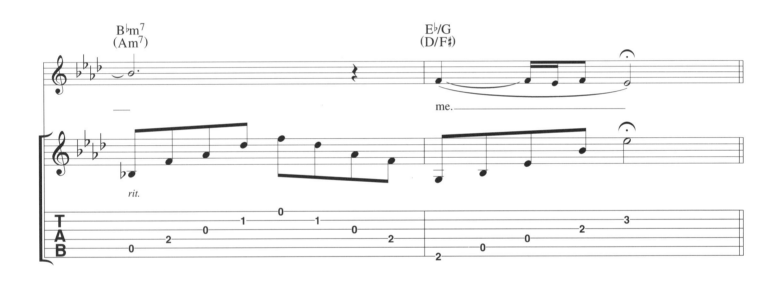

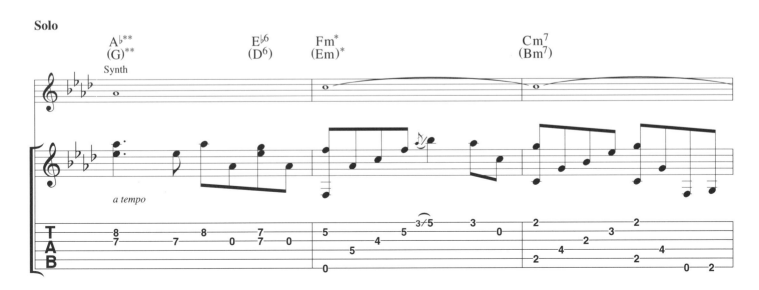

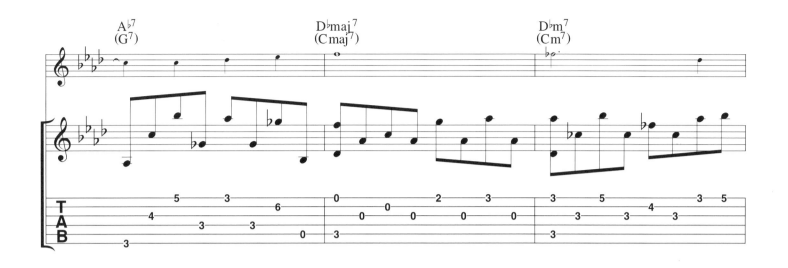

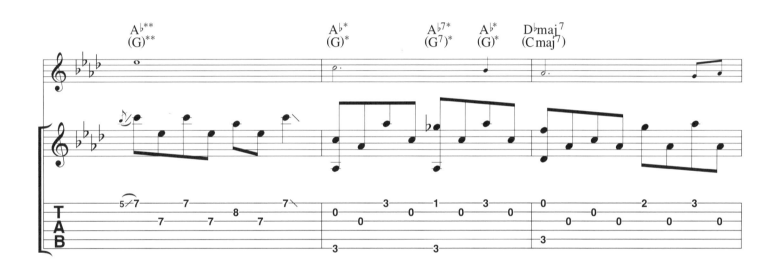

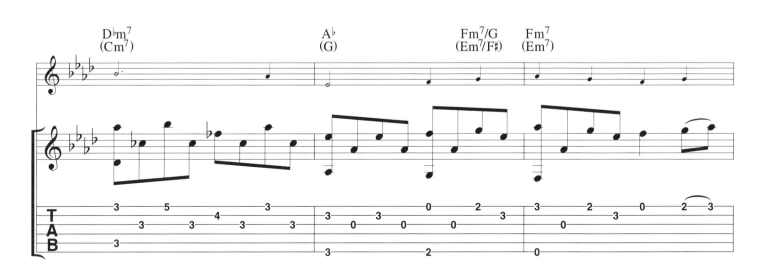

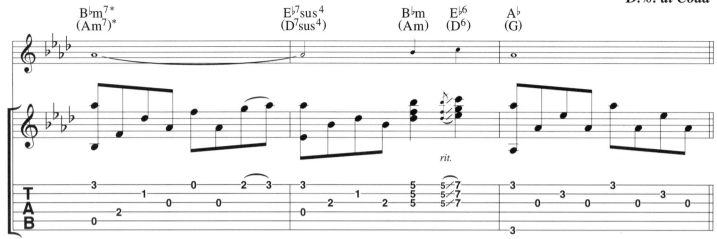

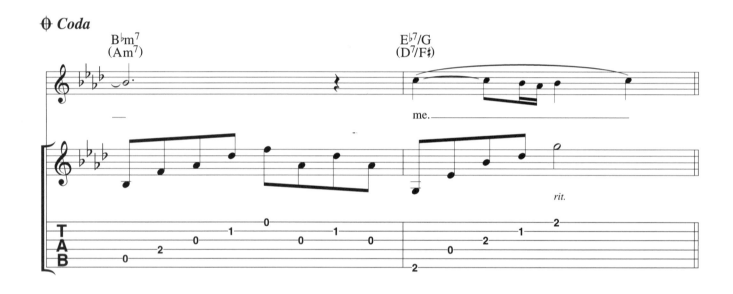

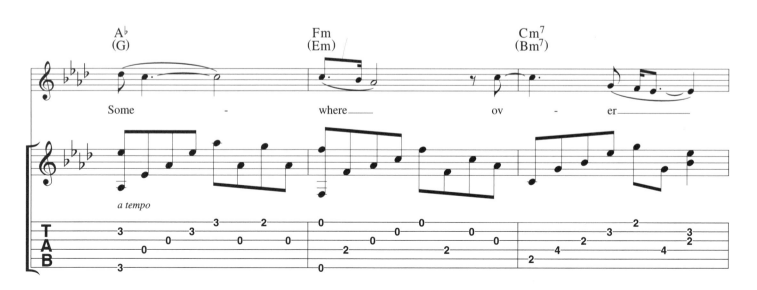

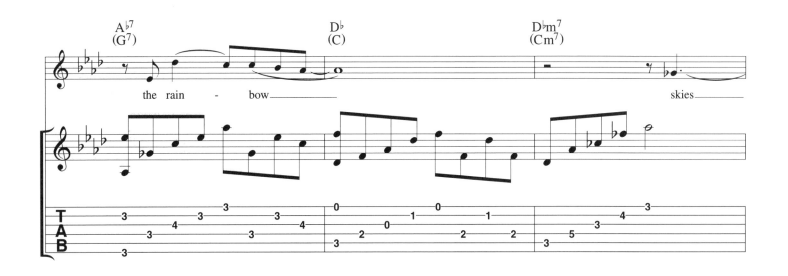

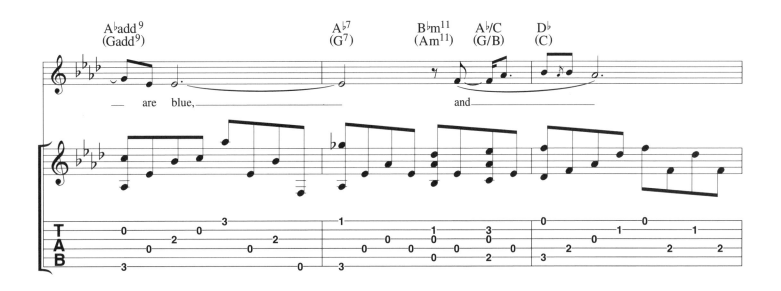

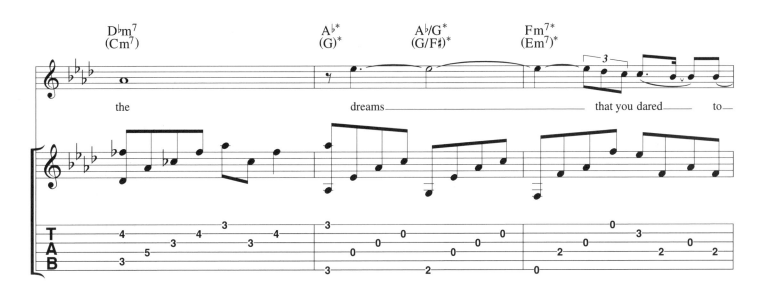

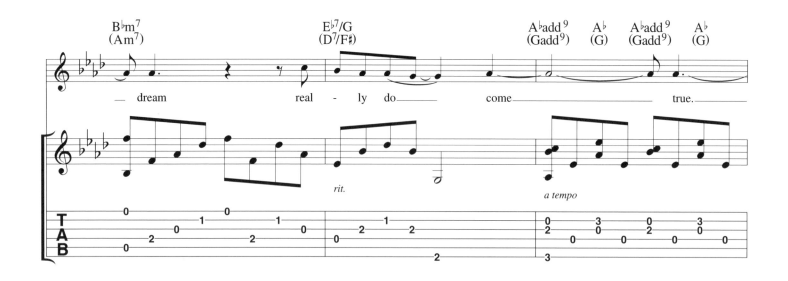

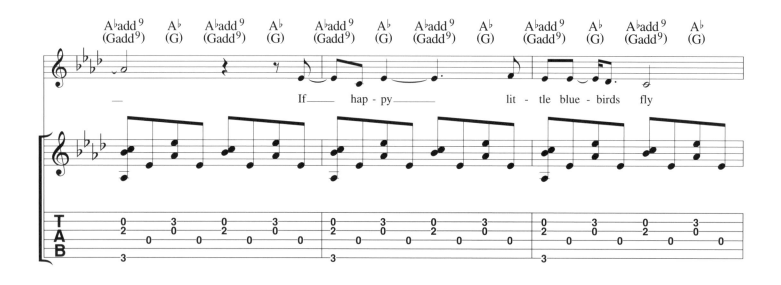

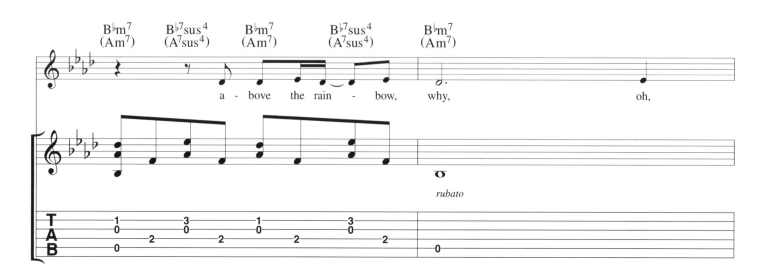

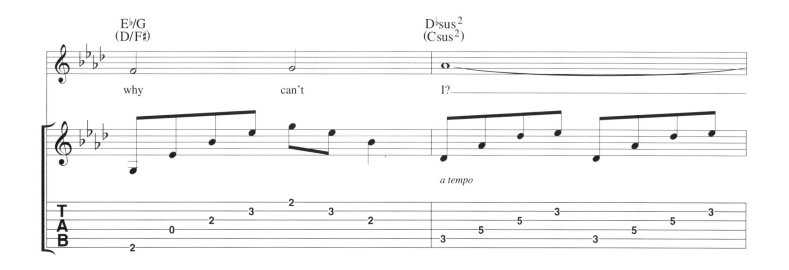

why   can't   I?

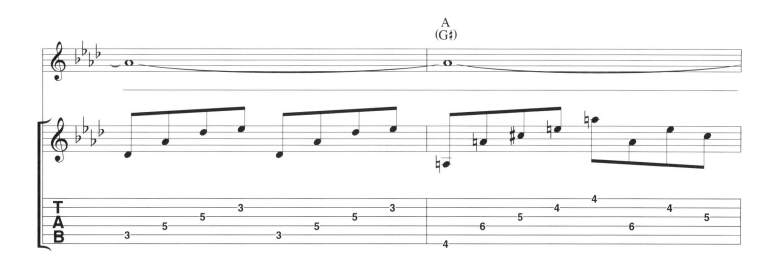

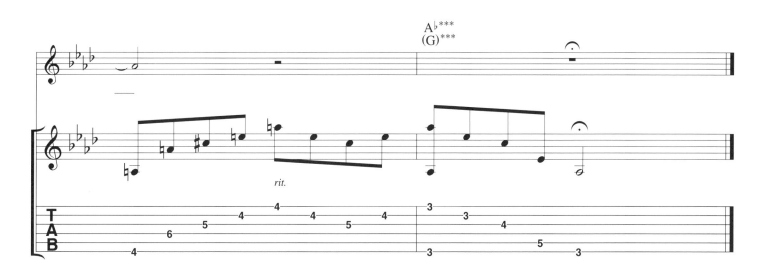

Présentation De La Tablature De Guitare

Il existe trois façons différentes de noter la musique pour guitare : à l'aide d'une portée musicale, de tablatures ou de barres rythmiques.

Les BARRES RYTHMIQUES sont indiquées au-dessus de la portée. Jouez les accords dans le rythme indiqué. Les notes rondes indiquent des notes réciles.

La PORTÉE MUSICALE indique les notes et rythmes et est divisée en mesures. Cette division est représentée par des lignes. Les notes sont : do, ré, mi, fa, sol, la, si.

La PORTÉE EN TABLATURE est une représentation graphique des touches de guitare. Chaque ligne horizontale correspond à une corde et chaque chiffre correspond à une case.

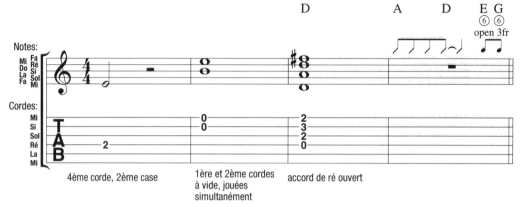

4ème corde, 2ème case — 1ère et 2ème cordes à vide, jouées simultanément — accord de ré ouvert

Notation Spéciale De Guitare : Définitions

TIRÉ DEMI-TON : Jouez la note et tirez la corde afin d'élever la note d'un demi-ton (étape à moitié).

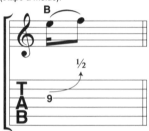

TIRÉ PLEIN : Jouez la note et tirez la corde afin d'élever la note d'un ton entier (étape entière).

TIRÉ D'AGRÉMENT : Jouez la note et tirez la corde comme indiqué. Jouez la première note aussi vite que possible.

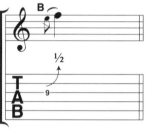

TIRÉ QUART DE TON : Jouez la note et tirez la corde afin d'élever la note d'un quart de ton.

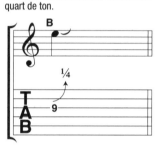

TIRÉ ET LÂCHÉ : Jouez la note et tirez la corde comme indiqué, puis relâchez, afin d'obtenir de nouveau la note de départ.

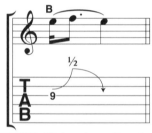

TIRÉ ET REJOUÉ : Jouez la note et tirez la corde comme indiqué puis rejouez la corde où le symbole apparaît.

PRÉ-TIRÉ : Tirez la corde comme indiqué puis jouez cette note.

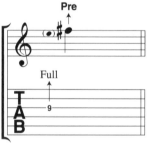

PRÉ-TIRÉ ET LÂCHÉ : Tirez la corde comme indiqué. Jouez la note puis relâchez la corde afin d'obtenir le ton de départ.

HAMMER-ON: Jouez la première note (plus basse) avec un doigt puis jouez la note plus haute sur la même corde avec un autre doigt, sur le manche mais sans vous servir du médiator.

PULL-OFF: Positionnez deux doigts sur les notes à jouer. Jouez la première note et sans vous servir du médiator, dégagez un doigt pour obtenir la deuxième note, plus basse.

GLISSANDO : Jouez la première note puis faites glisser le doigt le long du manche pour obtenir la seconde note qui, elle, n'est pas jouée.

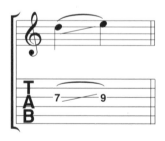

GLISSANDO ET REJOUÉ : Identique au glissando à ceci près que la seconde note est jouée.

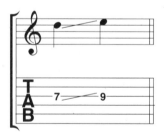

HARMONIQUES NATURELLES : Jouez la note tandis qu'un doigt effleure la corde sur le manche correspondant à la case indiquée.

PICK SCRAPE (SCRATCH) : On fait glisser le médiator le long de la corde, ce qui produit un son éraillé.

ÉTOUFFÉ DE LA PAUME : La note est partiellement étouffée par la main (celle qui se sert du médiator). Elle effleure la (les) corde(s) juste au-dessus du chevalet.

CORDES ÉTOUFFÉES : Un effet de percussion produit en posant à plat la main sur le manche sans relâcher, puis en jouant les cordes avec le médiator.

NOTE: La vitesse des tirés est indiquée par la notation musicale et le tempo.

Erläuterung zur Tabulaturschreibweise

Es gibt drei Möglichkeiten, Gitarrenmusik zu notieren: im klassichen Notensystem, in Tabulaturform oder als rhythmische Akzente.

RHYTHMISCHE AKZENTE werden über dem Notensystem notiert. Geschlagene Akkorde werden rhythmisch dargestellt. Ausgeschriebene Noten stellen Einzeltöne dar.

Im **NOTENSYSTEM** werden Tonhöhe und rhythmischer Verlauf festgelegt; es ist durch Taktstriche in Takte unterteilt. Die Töne werden nach den ersten acht Buchstaben des Alphabets benannt.
Beachte: "B" in der anglo-amerkanischen Schreibweise entspricht dem deutschen "H"!

DIE TABULATUR ist die optische Darstellung des Gitarrengriffbrettes. Jeder horizontalen Linie ist eine bestimmte Saite zugeordnet, jede Zahl bezeichnet einen Bund.

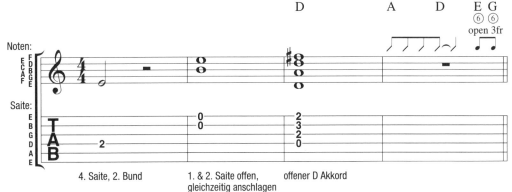

4. Saite, 2. Bund   1. & 2. Saite offen,   offener D Akkord
                           gleichzeitig anschlagen

Erklärungen zur speziellen Gitarennotation

HALBTON-ZIEHER: Spiele die Note und ziehe dann um einen Halbton höher (Halbtonschritt).

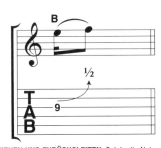

GANZTON-ZIEHER: Spiele die Note und ziehe dann einen Ganzton höher (Ganztonschritt).

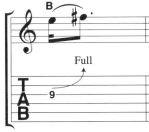

ZIEHER MIT VORSCHLAG: Spiele die Note und ziehe wie notiert. Spiele die erste Note so schnell wie möglich.

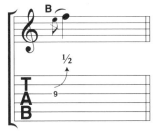

VIERTELTON-ZIEHER: Spiele die Note und ziehe dann einen Viertelton höher (Vierteltonschritt).

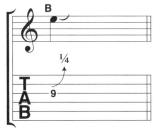

ZIEHEN UND ZURÜCKGLEITEN: Spiele die Note und ziehe wie notiert; lasse den Finger dann in die Ausgangposition zurückgleiten. Dabei wird nur die erste Note angeschlagen.

ZIEHEN UND NOCHMALIGES ANSCHLAGEN: Spiele die Note und ziehe wie notiert, schlage die Saite neu an, wenn das Symbol "▶" erscheint und lasse den Finger dann zurückgleiten.

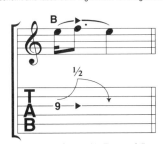

ZIEHER VOR DEM ANSCHLAGEN: Ziehe zuerst die Note wie notiert; schlage die Note dann an.

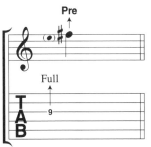

ZIEHER VOR DEM ANSCHLAGEN MIT ZURÜCKGLEITEN: Ziehe die Note wie notiert; schlage die Note dann an und lasse den Finger auf die Ausgangslage zurückgleiten.

AUFSCHLAGTECHNIK: Schlage die erste (tiefere) Note an; die höhere Note (auf der selben Saite) erklingt durch kräftiges Aufschlagen mit einem anderen Finger der Griffhand.

ABZIEHTECHNIK: Setze beide Finger auf die zu spielenden Noten und schlage die erste Note an. Ziehe dann (ohne nochmals anzuschlagen) den oberen Finger der Griffhand seitlich - abwärts ab, um die zweite (tiefere) Note zum klingen zu bringen.

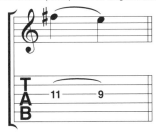

GLISSANDOTECHNIK: Schlage die erste Note an und rutsche dann mit dem selben Finger der Griffhand aufwärts oder abwärts zur zweiten Note. Die zweite Note wird nicht angeschlagen.

GLISSANDOTECHNIK MIT NACHFOLGENDEM ANSCHLAG: Gleiche Technik wie das gebundene Glissando, jedoch wird die zweite Note angeschlagen.

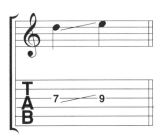

NATÜRLICHES FLAGEOLETT: Berühre die Saite über dem angegebenen Bund leicht mit einem Finger der Griffhand. Schlage die Saite an und lasse sie frei schwingen.

PICK SCRAPE: Fahre mit dem Plektrum nach unten über die Saiten - klappt am besten bei umsponnenen Saiten.

DÄMPFEN MIT DER SCHLAGHAND: Lege die Schlaghand oberhalb der Brücke leicht auf die Saite(n).

DÄMPFEN MIT DER GRIFFHAND: Du erreichst einen percussiven Sound, indem du die Griffhand leicht über die Saiten legst (ohne diese herunterzudrücken) und dann mit der Schlaghand anschlägst.

AMMERKUNG: Das Tempo der Zieher und Glissandos ist abhängig von der rhythmischen Notation und dem Grundtempo.

Tablatura De Guitarra Explicada

La música de guitarra puede ser representada en tres formas diferentes: en un pentagrama, en tablatura, y con acentos rítmicos.

ACENTOS RITMICOS están escritos sobre el pentagrama. Rasguea los acordes cuando te indique los acentos rítmicos. La aparición de una nota rodeada por un círculo indica una sola nota.

El PENTAGRAMA muestra la altura y el ritmo y está dividida en compases mediante unas líneas. La altura de las notas se denominan con las siete primeras notas del alfabeto.

TABLATURA representa gráficamente el diapasón de la guitarra. Cada línea horizontal representa una cuerda, y cada número representa un traste.

4ª Cuerda, 2º traste   1ª y 2ª cuerda al aire, tocadas a la vez   Acorde de D abierto

Definiciones Especiales Para La Notacion De Guitarra

BEND DE UN SEMITONO : Ataca la nota y eleva la cuerda hasta que esté medio tono por encima de la nota original (1/2 tono).

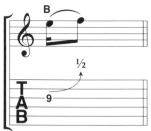

BEND DE UN TONO : Ataca la nota y eleva de la cuerda hasta que esté un tono por encima de la original (un tono completo).

BEND DE UNA NOTA RAPIDA (GRACE NOTE) : Ataca la nota y eleva la cuerda según se indique en la tablatura. Toca la primera nota tan rápidamente como te sea posible.

BEND DE UN CUARTO DE TONO : Ataca la nota y eleva la cuerda hasta que esté un cuarto de tono (1/4 tono) por encima de la original.

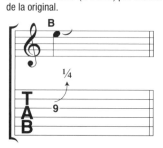

BEND & RELEASE : Ataca la nota y eleva la cuerda según se indica en la tablatura, regresa a la posición y nota iniciales.

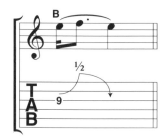

BEND & RESTRIKE: : Ataca la nota y eleva la cuerda según lo que indicado entonces ataca de nuevo la cuerda en la que aparece el símbolo.

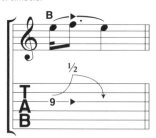

PRE-BEND : Eleva la cuerda según lo indicado, después atácala.

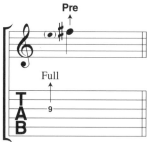

PRE-BEND & RELEASE : Eleva la cuerda según lo indicado. Atácala y regresa a la posición y nota original.

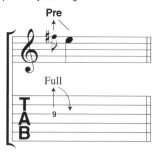

HAMMER-ON : Ataca una nota (grave) con un dedo, entonces haz sonar otra nota más aguda (en la misma cuerda) con otro dedo al tocarla directamente sobre el diapasón, sin atacar la cuerda de nuevo con la púa o los dedos.

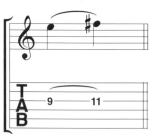

PULL-OFF: Sitúa los dedos sobre las notas que desees hacer sonar. Ataca la primera nota y sin utilizar la púa (o los dedos), retira el dedo para hacer que la segunda nota (más grave) suene.

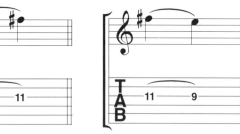

LEGATO SLIDE (GLISS) : Ataca la primera nota y entonces desliza el mismo dedo de la mano situada sobre el diapasón de forma ascendente o descendente hasta alcanzar la segunda nota. La segunda nota no se produce al ser atacada por los dedos o la púa.

SHIFT SLIDE (GLISS & RESTRIKE): Igual que el legato slide, excepto que la segunda nota se ataca con la púa o los dedos.

ARMÓNICOS NATURALES : Ataca la nota mientras que la mano situada sobre el diapasón roza ligeramente la cuerda directamente sobre el traste indicado.

RASPADO DE PÚA : El borde de la púa se desliza de forma descendente (o ascendente) por las cuerdas, provocando un sonido rasposo.

PALM MUTING : La nota es parcialmente apagada al apoyar la mano de la púa ligeramente sobre la cuerdas situándola justo antes del puente.

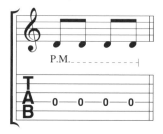

CUERDAS APAGADAS : Un sonido percusivo que se consigue al apoyar la mano situada sobre el diapasón sobre las cuerda (s) relajando la presión sobre éste, mientras que se ataca (n) con la otra mano.

NOTA : La velocidad de cualquier bend está indicada por la notación musical y el tempo.

10/02 (45539)